FARMING FACTS

AND

FAKE NEWS

LISTS ON ALL SORTS OF RURAL LIFE

FARMING FACTS
AND
FAKE NEWS
LISTS ON ALL SORTS OF RURAL LIFE

COMPILED BY
JOHN AND ANDREW ARBUCKLE

SOLD IN AID OF RSABI

Published in 2017 by
RSABI
Rural Centre
West Mains
Ingliston
Midlothian
EH28 8LT

ISBN: 9780992809034

British Library Cataloguing-in-Publication Data
A catalogue record for this book is available on request from the British Library.

Designed and typeset by Polaris Publishing, Edinburgh
www.polarispublishing.com

Printed by J Thomson, Glasgow

PREFACE

THERE HAS NEVER been a book of lists about farming and this aims to fill that gap. It covers the whole range of activities down on the farm and it stretches back into a previous era as well as recording what is happening today.

Reflecting modern life, some of the lists could be considered fake news but, unlike politicians who often mix up facts and fiction, we have every confidence in the reader recognising any strangers to the truth.

If you are looking for details on the biggest turnip or the heaviest yield of grain, this book is not for you. We have included many lists that may provoke an argument but few that will settle a dispute.

A word of warning, no attempt has been made to categorise the lists as we believe in the surprise element that comes from turning a page following a factual list to one which is entirely frivolous.

John and Andrew Arbuckle

THANKS

THIS BOOK WOULD not have been completed without the tremendous help of our friends who now hide round corners when they see us approach.

Special mention goes to Fordyce Maxwell, Ewan Pate, George Lawrie, Anne Ferrier, Patsy Hunter and Peter Small for their ideas, inspirations, corrections and generally keeping us on track.

Emma Penny has also done a tremendous job in proof reading, a specialist job.

Also thanks to Gordy Craw who has helped illustrate some of the more humorous issues contained within this volume.

And in the special thanks department, we include Victoria Pescodd and her colleagues in the Scottish Government who unearthed lots of information from the bowels of Government.

The mentioning of the above does not devalue help from those listed below. Frankly, without their efforts, there would be no book.

So thanks to Erika Hay, Bill Howatson, Judy McGowan, Keith Maxwell, Kate Richards, Donald Maxwell, Tom Maxwell, Posie & Tony Ridley, Carol McLaren, Keith Brand, Heather Wildman, Niall Bowser, Mags Granger, Tim Price, John Thomson, David Cranstoun, Jennifer Grant, Jack Lawson, Angus McKay, Sian Sharp, Ron & Joan Wilson, Jackie Henderson, Charlie Robertson, Finlay & Sophie Millar, Robin McIlrath, RSPB, John Marshall, Donald Biggar, Sue Stenner, Esther Green, Eddie Gillanders, Debbie Butcher, The Moredun Foundation, Dr Eleanor Harris, John Morton, Gemma Mackenzie, John Cameron, Heather Holmes, Jane Smernicki, Catherine Williamson, John Fife, Nicol McLaren, Graham Bruce, Aileen McFadzean, David Leggat, Arthur Anderson, Kenny Robertson, Martin Hall and Ronnie Black.

CONTENTS

FOREWORD

ON MY TRAVELS north of the border I have been delighted to support RSABI from time to time and the great charitable work it does supporting people in Scottish agriculture. It seems to me that Andrew and John Arbuckle's latest book is worthy indeed of all our backing, with proceeds going to such an excellent cause. It will sit proudly on my bookshelf at home alongside my copy of *Farming is a Funny Business*.

I much enjoyed reflecting upon my own choices for the rare breed list kindly included within these pages, and whether or not to include a favourite breed of my own from the Highlands. While not rare, it is wonderful to have our own Scottish Royal bull at the Cotswold Farm Park! Well done too, to the many individual contributors who join me on the pages that follow.

The authors have undoubtedly compiled a fascinating collection of farming related material that I am sure will appeal widely to folk up and down the country – I am pleased to wholeheartedly commend the book to you and hope you enjoy reading it as much as I have.

Thank you for supporting the important work undertaken by the charity – RSABI deserves all our help and I know that the funds raised will be put to good use.

Adam Henson, July 2017

Photograph courtesy of *Scottish Farmer*

CHAPTER ONE

ADAM HENSON'S TOP TEN LIVESTOCK BREEDS

Adam Henson is known throughout the UK for his enthusiastic support for the farming industry. His own roots include being brought up on the family farm where his father kept a range of rare breeds. Below are ten of Adam's favourite breeds:

1. Cotswold sheep – one of my dad's earliest breeds in his collection. The Cotswold sheep grazed the local area in their thousands and gave the region its name. 'Cote' refers to a sheep enclosure and 'Wold' the rolling hills. Known as the 'Cotswold Lion', their long lustrous wool was termed the 'Golden Fleece' and helped pay for many of the local manor houses and churches.

2. Gloucester cattle – a beautiful docile animal, mahogany in colour with a distinctive white tail. Single Gloucester cheese can only be produced on farms in Gloucestershire where they have Gloucester cows, giving it a similar prestige to Champagne (which can only be produced in the Champagne region).

3. Gloucestershire Old Spot – hardy, cheery and even-tempered, the Gloucestershire Old Spot is the oldest pedigree spotted pig in the world. Legend says that their spots were caused by falling apples in the orchards of the Severn Valley where they grazed. They provide deliciously succulent pork, bacon and sausages.

4. North Ronaldsay sheep – this little seaweed-eating breed was isolated on one island in the Orkneys. At the age of eight I went with my dad, Joe Henson, to buy another island on behalf of the Rare Breeds Survival Trust, moving a flock onto it and bringing one hundred sheep south to England. This spread the breed out geographically to keep them safe from disease or natural disaster. It was a trip I will never forget.

5. Chillingham cattle – this remarkable breed survives as a feral herd in Chillingham Park in Northumberland. I have had the great privilege to get up close to them with the ranger when filming with Countryfile. The bulls fight for their hierarchy and to win cows with lots of roaring and pawing the ground. It's like stepping back in time to when these animals were first enclosed and knights would hunt them on horseback with dogs and a spear.

6. Berkshire pigs – in 2016 we decided to introduce another rare breed of pig to the Cotswold Farm Park, one particularly suited to our animal handling area. Fran in our livestock team recommended Berkshires, known as the ladies pig because they are small with a good temperament. Black all over apart from six white points, one on each foot, a stripe on the forehead and the tip of their tail, they are perfect for the job and children and adults alike adore them.

7. White Faced Dartmoor sheep – Mike Caunter, our livestock manager, is a Devon boy with a longstanding connection to these sheep and persuaded me to try some. We went to Devon to buy from a breeder and well-known Dartmoor poet Colin Creese. As is often the case, Countryfile was following my journey. The final piece on the programme had Colin narrating one of his poems with wonderful shots of the moor and sheep. They are fantastic, hardy little sheep and great mothers.

8. Longhorns – these cattle are a rare breed success story as they have become so popular they are no longer rare. We had them on the farm for many years and my sister Libby was the society secretary, having a lot to do with their promotion and success. My fondest two were a pair of working oxen trained to pull a cart that starred in the film Braveheart with Mel Gibson. I had to get dressed in a kilt and ginger wig to work alongside the actors in case the oxen misbehaved. My claim to fame is being directed by Mel Gibson.

9. Castlemilk Moorit sheep – these are a very lively breed and perhaps not the easiest to work with, however they look fantastic and my father was responsible for saving them from extinction. They are a primitive breed with horns in both ewe and ram and moorit coloured, meaning mousey brown. They were originally created by Sir Buchanan-Jardine on his Castlemilk Estate in Dumfriesshire, using Manx Loghtan, Moorit, Shetland and wild Mouflon to create a breed that would provide fine, kemp-free moorit-coloured wool. When he died, most of the flock was culled, however a few were dispersed including six ewes and a ram which my father bought. All of today's Castlemilk Moorits are descended from these few dispersed sheep and we still have them on the farm today.

10. Highland Cattle – these are not and have never been a rare breed but must have a mention as they are a favourite of mine. Their long shaggy coats protect them from all the Highland weather can throw at them. The hardiest of British breeds they come in a range of colours including red, black, dun, brindled and yellow. I had the great pleasure of buying a young bull from the Balmoral Estate in Scotland, owned by Her Majesty the Queen, so we now have a royal bull at the Cotswold Farm Park.

TEN OF MY FAVOURITE THINGS PRODUCED BY SCOTTISH FARMERS AND CROFTERS, BY RURAL ECONOMY SECRETARY FERGUS EWING

1. The delicious meats – from Scotch Beef and Scotch Lamb to chicken and turkey – just some of the fine Scottish produce specially recognised by PGI status, protected across Europe against imitations.

2. The healthy fruit and veg that make a meal, especially Scottish strawberries and raspberries which are increasingly available for most of the year.

3. Our fantastic dairy produce – whether it's delicious cheeses with oatcakes, a yogurt or a dash of Scottish milk in a cup of tea or coffee.

4. Whether it's a woolly jumper, blanket or the stuffing for mattresses, the wool our farmers produce helps to keep us warm and comfortable in a cold Scottish winter.

5. The beautiful countryside that our farmers are guardians of. Our spectacular landscape is one of the things we are renowned for, and being out and about in rural Scotland is truly breath-taking and always inspiring.

6. Some of the stunning residences and heritage in our rural areas – everything from traditional farm houses handed down with the farm through the generations to castles and ruins to modern takes on blackhouses and cottages.

7. The simple spirit of innovation and resilience that is common across Scottish agriculture and has led to many exciting diversification schemes, producing cafes, outdoor play centres, holiday accommodation and renewable energy opportunities to name a few.

8. The many artisan items produced and inspired by farming families that you can buy in our farm shops and which play an increasing role in our food and drink success story.

9. The cows, sheep, horses and other animals our farmers take care of – you can't fail to be impressed by a walk around the livestock area at one of our many agricultural shows.

10. Perhaps my favourite of all, a wee dram or two of Scotch!

NATIONAL FARMERS UNION OF SCOTLAND ACHIEVEMENTS

The National Farmers Union of Scotland has been in existence for more than one hundred years and during that time has fought hundreds of campaigns on behalf of its members. Among the more memorable are:

1. Marketing Boards – established in 1933 following years when imports had almost crushed the home industry. Less than a decade later, the importance of home production proved critical in feeding the country and winning the Second World War.

2. Eradication of animal diseases – the union played a major role in campaigning and acting to eradicate a number of livestock diseases. One of the most notable successes was the eventual control of the 2001 foot and mouth outbreak where the union played a major role in the co-ordination of the effort north of the border.

3. Extreme weather – while it has no control over the weather, the union has, on numerous occasions over the years, either co-ordinated relief operations in disaster areas or has helped gain compensation for climatic extremes.

4. Less Favoured Areas – the union ensured that Scotland's hill and island areas were recognised when the UK entered the EC and has continued to fight for those farming in our more challenging environments.

5. 'The Green Pound' – for twenty years from the 1970s to the 1990s the injustice of the 'green pound' disparity had to be fought. This anomaly saw UK producers get up to 40% less for their pigmeat, cereals, milk and beef than their continental counterparts.

6. French lamb ban – the union fought the French over their illegal ban on importing Scottish sheep meat. This was a long but ultimately successful campaign.

7. Beef imports from Ireland and South America were causing damage to home producers. This was addressed initially by organising demonstrations at Stranraer and Merklands and eventually by negotiations.

8. Barley imports by distillers undermined the home market. The union campaigned against these in 2002, but the first protest was back in 1925 when Nairn County NFU asked for a tax to be imposed on all foreign barley delivered to distilleries.

9. Representation in Brussels – along with other unions in the UK, NFUS set up an office in Brussels when the UK joined the Common Market. This ensured that Scottish matters were considered in all European discussions.

TOP TATTIE VARIETIES

Hundreds of potato varieties are grown in this country as consumers have their own preferences in what they want from the spuds on their plates. Among the more common and recognisable ones are:

1. Maris Piper – it may be more than fifty years since it came on the market but it is still leading the way in the popularity stakes, with everyone from chip shops to processors helping to ensure the variety accounts for one acre in every six grown.

2. Markies – another but much more recent variety in all-round demand, but its second place on the list is largely due to processing demand.

3. Maris Peer – a variety to come out of the Plant Breeding Institute in the 1960s, this second-early produces an even sample of smooth skinned tatties.

4. Lady Rosetta – has been the mainstay for the English frozen chip trade, but despite holding on to the title of fourth most popular variety in Great Britain, this Dutch bred potato is now losing popularity.

5. Estima – now fading from the scene after being very popular, however this Dutch bred variety is still liked by the supermarkets.

6. Melody – another Dutch-bred entrant which is proving popular with the supermarket trade.

7. Harmony – Scottish bred by Jack Dunnett of Caithness Potatoes. A prepacker but also in demand generally.

8. Marfona – Dutch bred variety that is the source of many of the 'baker' potatoes on the market.

9. Hermes – Austrian bred variety which now dominates in the important crisping trade.

10. King Edward – still in the top ten most popular varieties despite being bred more than one hundred years ago. Susceptible to most diseases but still seen as the quality potato.

TOP OF THE CAP SUBSIDY LIST IN 2015

No longer with us and largely unlamented, the Single Farm Payment scheme allowed farmers to accumulate large amounts of subsidies. The top recipients in this list in 2015 were:

1. The National Trust – £8,056,505
The National Trust in England owns and cares for 71,630 acres itself, but owns 618,000 in total which is farmed by 2,000 tenants. Its ownership accounts for 25% of the Lake District and 10% of the Peak District.

2. RSPB – £3,584,032
Its 200 nature reserves cover 321,237 acres of UK land and its 124,000 acres in Scotland makes it the eighth largest landowner in Scotland.

3. Frank A. Smart & Son – £2,986,506
This company owned 39 farms in Speyside in 2013; Mr Smart was farming 87,423 acres across Scotland and was reckoned to be far and away the largest farmer in the UK. He also had the unenviable moniker of 'King of the slipper farmers'.

4. Farmcare Trading Ltd – £1,784,647
Known as The Co-operative Farms until it was sold to the Wellcome Trust in 2014 for £249m. At the time of sale, The Co-operative Farms owned 39,533 acres on 15 farms.

5. Blankney Farms Ltd – £1,690,111
This is a large holding in Metheringham, Lincolnshire, owned by the Parker family. It runs to 14,000 acres growing a wide range of arable crops for human consumption, animal feed and energy production.

6. Beeswax Farming (Rainbow) Ltd – £1,546,462
Sir James Dyson, the vacuum cleaner tycoon, paid some £150m for 17,000 acres in 2013. The land includes much of the Nocton estate near Lincoln.

7. R.J., T.J. and M.T. Feakins – £1,270,282
Robin Feakins and his family farm several farms near Bonchester Bridge in the Borders. This award represents easily the largest single farm payment for any agricultural operation in the Borders.

8. Strutt & Parker (Farms) Ltd – £1,227,909
The company owns four management units in South East England with a total area of 19,500 acres. More than 80% of the land is farmed under a long-term tenancy agreement.

RURAL HEALTH PROBLEMS

Life in the countryside is widely considered to be healthy. Do not believe that for a minute. The following ailments beset rural residents much more than their urban cousins.

1. Farmer's lung – a non-infectious allergic disease caused by inhaling spores from mouldy hay, straw or grain.

2. Weil's disease – a bacterial infection which can be contracted by coming into contact with the bodily fluids ie urine, blood or tissue of animals, especially rats, that are already infected.

3. Noise-induced hearing loss – a condition widely experienced now some 50 years after ear protectors should have been worn by all those driving a tractor with a rotavator behind going at full revs, standing next to a hammer mill watching grain being bruised or working on a potato grader.

4. Lower back pain – caused by carrying heavy grain sacks away from threshing mill a long time before the maximum weight for one person lift was 25 kilos. Foolish competitions saw men lift two fifty six pound weights – total of 50 kilos – above their heads. Another culprit in the sore back stakes was pulling neeps.

5. Mental health problems – only now being recognised, with many variations related to the physical environment, structure of farming families, economic difficulties and uncertainties associated with farming.

6. Brucellosis – in cattle, this is known as contagious abortion but in humans it is known as undulant fever. It used to be endemic in the veterinary profession but has now slipped down the agenda. This is a notifiable disease which has been eradicated from cattle in Great Britain, but there is still a danger from imported animals.

7. Ringworm – one of the most common skin diseases of cattle. Infective spores remain viable for months in soil, bedding and for years on halters and barn surfaces. It is also easily transmitted to humans by contact with infected animals or any of the above.

8. Orf – a viral disease where those who work with sheep are vulnerable as it can be transmitted from infected stock.

WOMEN WHO HAVE MADE THE BIGGEST IMPACT ON SCOTTISH AGRICULTURE IN THE PAST CENTURY
Note: not in order

While traditionally agriculture has been male dominated, women are increasingly rising to the top. Among the female leaders are:

1. Julie Fitzpatrick – principal and director of the Moredun Research Institute and an eminent scientist in her own right.

2. Marion Tilson – stalwart of the Aberdeen Angus breed. The Wedderlie herd's roots stretch back to 1913.

3. Betty MacDonald – convenor of the Crofting Committee of the National Farmers Union of Scotland in the 1970s. Crofter and character in her community in Ardnamurchan.

4. Fiona Dalrymple – chaired the pigs committee of the National Farmers Union of Scotland in the late 1970s. Worked hard for the pig industry in difficult times.

5. Sarah Mackie – from an Aberdeenshire farming family she made her way in the tough supermarket world before setting up her own food consultancy.

6. Flora Stuart – throughout her life she promoted the Belted Galloway breed and, as a result, there are Beltie herds all over the world.

7. Jo Durno – former chairman of the Highlands and Island committee of the NFU of Scotland. Awarded John Miskelly award for her contribution to the union.

8. Sybil MacPherson – former chairman of the National Sheep Association of Scotland and star of 'This Farming Life' reality TV show, part of which was shot on her farm in the West Highlands.

9. Nina Clancy – first female chief executive of the rural charity RSABI.

10. Sheila Voas – Scottish Chief Veterinary Officer. Worked in general practice before working for the Scottish Government.

11. Mary Durno – from Uppermill, Tarves. Kept the old-established Uppermill Beef Shorthorn herd going following the death of her father, Dr James Durno.

12. Patsy Hunter – over the past twenty years, she has established herself as the most knowledgeable and industrious reporter in the Scottish livestock industry.

13. Bright Gordon – from Rosefarm on the Black Isle, which she took over on D-Day. A noted potato and cereal producer, she was a Potato Marketing Board member for eight years, a director of Buchan Meat Producers and of Scottish Plant Breeders.

14. Fiona Burnett – specialist in crop disease and management at SRUC, with an increasing focus on managing fungicide resistance. Manages the SRUC crop clinic too, keeping farmers and advisers up to date with risks.

15. Ena Baxter – maybe a little removed from direct agriculture, but her use of locally-sourced Scottish produce was a key factor in Baxters' global success.

MOST COMMON FARMER RESPONSES TO "HOW ARE YOU?"

1. "Oh living the dream" – said with sarcasm when the questioned one is clearly not.

2. "Oh just hingin t'gither" – said with slight understatement.

3. "Well, I'm still here, what's left of me that is" – as above, or for the older ones: "It's better than the alternative".

4. "Every day's a bonus" – back to the heavy sarcasm.

5. "Bloody awful, what's the world coming to with Brexit, Trump, global warming" – one for the real pessimists.

6. "Could do with some decent weather" – whether it be sun, drouth or rain the farmer is needing this will be the most common response.

7. "Well I was fine, but the baler/combine/loader has just packed in" – a signal that the farmer has no time to stand and blether with you.

FARMING NURSERY RHYMES

Which parent, or grandparent, hasn't endured a car journey without going through Old Macdonald's Farm from cat to rat, and from donkey to monkey?

The following is a list of rhymes, or songs which were conceived on the land, born out of a child's need for repetition and rhythm. They have all stood the test of time and countless generations.

1. *Baa baa black sheep* Genial and talkative sheep shares its wool locally.

2. *Ding dong dell, pussy's in the well* Unruly youth throws local mouser into the water supply.

3. *Mary had a little lamb* All about the perils of taking on a pet lamb. It is a lesson still appropriate to the present day.

4. *The farmer's in his den* But he is not there on his own for long as he builds up the farm stock.

5. *Goosey goosey gander* This includes good advice about taking the farm's goose into the farm house.

6. *To market to market to buy a fat pig* Nowadays much leaner pigs are in vogue but the benefits of the local farmers' market are obvious.

7. *Three blind mice* A pretty bloody tale proving the farmer's wife is always a force to be reckoned with.

8. *For the want of a nail* Long before buck passing and box ticking became prevalent, this tale blamed the blacksmith.

9. *Hickety pickety my black hen* Sexist bird only laid eggs for gentlemen. A prolific but picky layer.

10. *This is the house that Jack built* Early proof of the benefits of co-operation.

Hickety Pickety My Black Hen

Choosey layer

BREEDS NO LONGER SHOWN AT THE HIGHLAND SHOW

Breeds of livestock are susceptible to changes in demand and among those that have slipped down the popularity stakes are:

1. Romagnola – this Italian breed of cattle with wild ox genes in its breeding came over to the UK in the flood of breeds in the second half of last century. Some breeds flourished and now dominate the UK livestock industry but this one did not.

2. Dorset Horn – this South of England sheep breed gained a certain popularity in the middle of last century on account of its unique ability to breed throughout the year, but it has now largely faded from the scene.

3. Shropshire – this English breed of sheep with the oldest flock record book among all the breeds made a brief appearance at the Highland show in the 1930s.

4. Red Poll cattle – this dual-purpose breed achieved a degree of popularity between the wars but faded away as farming became more specialised.

5. Fife – while there were representatives of this cattle breed at the first ever Highland Show in 1822, these small black animals soon lost out to larger framed cattle. The breed is now extinct.

6. Large White – along with Welsh Blacks, Middle Whites and Tamworths, these breeds of pigs slipped from the showing schedule as a result of increased biosecurity in the pig industry, greater use of hybrids and pigs' susceptibility to disease, especially foot and mouth.

7. Southdown – one of the oldest sheep breeds around, having been established more than 200 years ago. Still popular in parts of England and very prominent in the Highland Shows of early last century, their numbers have now dwindled.

8. Shetland cattle – shown at the Highland in the early years of last century, this hardy breed slipped down to being 'critically endangered' by the end of it. The breed is now making a recovery thanks to niche marketing and use on conservation sites.

9. Murray Grey – this Australian breed was imported in the 1970s, and appeared at the Highland Show. There are still a number of enthusiasts supporting this breed where the emphasis is on easy care and easy calving cows.

10. Bedfordshire – despite winning the pig championship at the first ever Highland Show, this breed appears to have vanished altogether.

BEST NON-FICTION BOOKS ABOUT FARMING

1. Peter Kerr: *Thistle Soup*
A compelling story of four generations of farmers who move from Orkney to Cuddy Neuk Farm in East Lothian on the outbreak of World War II.

2. Alexander Fenton: *Scottish Country Life*
A ground-breaking work by one of Scotland's leading rural scholars which offers a highly readable picture of historical change through the eyes of the people themselves, the tools they used and the food they ate.

3. A.G. Street: *The Endless Furrow*
A peerless contribution to the history of farming in early 20th century England by writer, broadcaster and farmer Street, who was the author of a series of acclaimed works.

4. A.G. Street: *Farmer's Glory*
Another entry by the same author, it details farming in the 1930s.

5. John Cherrington: *On the Smell of an Oily Rag*
His tale of coming into farming is well told and it includes his opposition to farm subsidies and the CAP.

6. John Stewart Collis: *The Worm Forgives the Plough*
This book, about an academic turned ploughman, sold over two million copies, and has been hailed as a landmark piece of work from an environmental point of view.

7. James Hunter: *The Making of the Crofting Community*
The seminal work which tells the story of the forces that shaped modern crofting, and which offered the crofters a voice based on sound research.

8. John R. Allan: *Farmer's Boy*
A rich portrait of farming in North-east Scotland through the eyes of a child by an inspired and mature author even in his early years. This book has endured as an evocative and sensitive portrait of farm and rural life.

9. Thomas Firbank: *I Bought a Mountain*
A young man buys 5,000 acres of Snowdonia. He survives and prospers.

10. Adrian Bell: *Corduroy*
The first of a classic trilogy of biography which narrates the changing farming world in the 1930s and 40s by the father of internationally recognised journalist, Martin Bell.

11. Ronald Blythe: *Akenfield*
The seminal study of change and tradition in rural Sussex which painted a graphic and stark picture of country life and social class. Published in 1969 to widespread acclaim it has stood the test of time as a classic text.

13. Henry Williamson: *Story of a Norfolk Farm*
By the author of Tarka the Otter and many more novels, this biography from the hungry 30s describes buying a run-down Norfolk farm and his struggle in knocking it into shape.

14. Richard Benson: *The Farm*
The author leaves his native Yorkshire to work as a journalist in London. He has to come home to save the family farm, and his story is a moving personal account, but also one that reflects a profound change in rural life.

CHAPTER TWO

FORMER TRACTOR FACTORIES

The UK used to be one of the major tractor manufacturers in the world and even to this day, many old tractors built in this country are working in fields across the globe.

1. Banner Lane – this massive site on the outskirts of Coventry was first used to build Bristol Hercules aircraft engines during the Second World War. Post-war, the Standard Motor Co. headed by Sir John Black took over the factory and came to an agreement to build Harry Ferguson's revolutionary tractor, eventually using Standard engines. By 1959 the new Massey Ferguson concern bought the factory and had assembled more than three million tractors before it was closed in 2002. Today it is a housing development.

2. Kilmarnock – Massey Harris was attracted to Ayrshire largely because of the availability of a workforce that was already skilled in engineering. The plant was in full production from 1949, later becoming a Massey Ferguson plant. The Massey Harris 744 tractor, the 726 and 780 combines and 701 baler and several other implements were made there, before the creation of MF – several of its lines were manufactured there until it closed in 1980. The site is largely still standing today.

3. Dagenham – Edsel Ford, Henry Ford's son, cut the first sod here in 1929. This giant plant, covering 475 acres, saw the production of cars, commercial vehicles, industrial equipment engines and tractors. In World War II, the Fordson range which was made here represented 95% of UK tractor production. Ford moved its tractor production to Basildon in 1964. Other vehicle production at Dagenham dwindled and today only engines are produced.

4. Meltham – David Brown's first tractor of its own design – following an unsuccessful arrangement with Harry Ferguson – was produced at this former spinning mill. Production began just as war was declared and continued alongside other war work. After the war, David Brown brought out a succession of tractors, rising to become the UK's third largest manufacturer. It was bought by Case in 1972, and after Case bought out International in 1984 Meltham's days were numbered, with the last tractor being completed in 1988. Today the site produces gearboxes for several other makes of tractor.

5. Doncaster – this plant was the UK headquarters of the International Harvester Company. Initially implements were manufactured here, then tractors in 1949 with the McCormick-International Farmall 'M'. This was followed by a long line of IH and Case IH models until the Case IH New Holland merger where, under European competition law, the plant was sold to Agri Argo which produced its range of McCormick machines until it moved production to Italy. The site has now been developed for housing.

6. Essendine – the factory near Stamford began manufacturing Minneapolis Moline tractors after the war, before Allis Chalmers moved here from Totton near Southampton in 1949. Production of the Allis Chalmers Model B D270, D272 and ED40 continued until 1969. Combine production continued for a further two years before Allis Chalmers pulled out of the UK. Much of the factory has been adopted for other uses today.

7. Gainsborough – Marshall's, an old established agricultural engineering company, launched the single cylinder diesel tractor15/30 (Model E) in 1930 which became the Model M in 1938. This developed into the Field Marshall in 1944 before wheeled tractor production ceased in 1956. Track Marshall crawler production then moved here, and in 1982 Charles Nickerson who now owned Track Marshall bought the Leyland tractor division and moved production here under the Marshall name. Production did not last too long before it moved to Scunthorpe, leaving Gainsborough largely unused. Today it is a supermarket complex.

8. Fleet – the firm of County Commercial Cars started tractor production here by converting Fordson Majors into crawler tractors. It progressed to making equal-sized four-wheel drive tractors from Ford skid units, inventing several different variations and specialist machines along the way. It built more than 30,000 machines from 1948 to 1983 when it went onto receivership after Ford started to offer factory fitted 4WD versions.

9. Bradford – in 1954 the International Harvester Company purchased the Jowett Motor Company works at Bradford and converted to production of B250 tractors. It built its smaller models until 1982 when production ended. Today the site is a supermarket.

10. Wolverhampton – The Turner Manufacturing Company built a tractor called the 'Yeoman of England', fitted with a V4 '2V95' diesel engine. Tractors were built there from 1949 to 1957. It was advertised as 'being able to pull four furrows as easily as other tractors could pull three because of its astonishing lugging power'. Nevertheless, it developed an unenviable reputation as being a difficult starter alongside other reliability issues. Turner continued with many other engineering projects and was involved with tractor transmission components in the 1970s. Today Turner is owned by Caterpillar.

11. Longbridge – in 1918 Herbert Austin began designing his own tractor based on the Fordson at Longbridge, Birmingham. Though more expensive than the Fordson it enjoyed a brief period of popularity from 1919 to 1924. With the advent of the popular car, the Austin 7, production had to concentrate on cars and tractor production was moved to France. Longbridge closed following the sale of MG to China and the site has been redeveloped.

WORST JOBS IN FARMING

Farming is not all working in the sunshine with little birds singing in the trees as the harvest is gathered in. The following is a list of less enjoyable activities down on the farm:

1. Gathering stones – this used to be a regular springtime job on many arable farms with stoney soils. Not a single brain cell was needed for this most monotonous task.

2. Picking rotten potatoes off the grader – it has always been essential to remove rotten tatties before they smear others at grading time, but it is a rotten job picking up the slobbery spuds.

3. Lifting the last sheaves from a stack or the bottom row of bales – both guaranteed to result in rats and mice scurrying away in haste for a new shelter

4. Lambing an already dead lamb – apart from dealing with the loss of a lamb, there is the physical difficulty of removing a body from its mother's womb.

5. Roguing blackleg – one for the seed potato producers. This can be a task of Biblical proportions made worse by knowing it is not effective, only cosmetic.

6. Roguing wild oats on a wet muggy day – a combination of monotony and being very uncomfortable.

7. Pulling runches (charlock) from a field of turnips – completing a trio of crop husbandry horrors, this is every bit as tedious and tiresome as the two above.

8. Trying to get a calf/lamb to suck – especially when the newly born animal does not seem to be interested.

9. Testing the electric fence – well someone has to do it.

10. Herding newly weaned lambs out of a field with no dog or quad bike.

11. Trying to get a ewe to accept her own lamb(s) which for some reason she has rejected.

12. Covering silage clamps – the most effective method of doing so involves using old tyres but these often contain stagnant water after lying around the stackyard.

13. Locating and dealing with burst field drain – this is one for experts only. Often carried out in bad weather.

14. Cleaning out the grain dryer – a combination of dust and vermin make this a pretty unpleasant job.

15. Defrosting water pipes – a job that has to be carried out with care. Otherwise it can become 'repairing burst water pipes'.

16. Repairing a water filled tyre – in a farming variation of Murphy's Law, punctures always seem to occur at the furthest point from the farm steading, thus adding difficulty to an already tough job.

17. Trying to refit a dual wheel in the dark on a hillside while drilling grain – a personal experience of Fordyce Maxwell.

18. Cleaning out a blocked septic tank – usually necessary when dressed ready to go out to some meeting. Remedial work cannot be put off.

19. Office work – unless avoiding any of the above tasks, this is the least favourite job for many farmers.

Testing the Electric Fence

Better trying it with a blade of grass

BUSINESSES NO LONGER WITH US

As farming changes so do the companies that work in the industry. For various reasons, the following once significant companies are no longer with us.

1. North Eastern Farmers – this major co-operative based in Aberdeenshire closed its doors in the mid 1990s after a series of loss-making years. It was one of the original farm co-ops.

2. Gordon & Innes potato merchants, Fochabers left behind a multi-million pound debt as its doors clanged shut in 2000. The company assets were taken over by Higgins of Doncaster.

3. Buchan Meat Producers, Turriff went into receivership in 1996 with creditors totalling £4 million. The business was bought over by Irish firm Kepak.

4. Golden Wonder crisp factory. The company was founded by Edinburgh baker William Alexander. At its peak, there were five factories including one in West Lothian. This closed because the sugars in Scottish potatoes were often higher than further south in the UK and high sugars lead to black crisps.

5. Central Farmers, Methil, Fife operated as an agricultural supply company from 1926 to 2000 when its assets were bought over by Carrs Billington.

6. Scottish Agricultural Industries (SAI) based at Leith was a powerhouse in the agricultural supply business in the post-Second World War era. The company was a subsidiary of Imperial Chemical Industries (ICI) and closed when the parent company hit hard times.

7. Lawsons of Dyce was a big player in pig processing – allegedly using every part of the pig except the squeak. The company was taken over by Walls. Processing and curing ceased in 1973.

8. Vion took over the Grampian Country Food Group, controlling a number of meat processing plants in Scotland but this Dutch owned co-operative retreated from Scotland in 2012 with the loss of thousands of jobs.

9. A large number of smaller machinery manufacturers and dealerships have disappeared over the years as businesses have had to grow larger to survive in a competitive world. Many farms will have had a Grays of Fetterangus roller, for instance.

LESSER KNOWN HIGHLAND SHOW VENUES

Until it settled at its permanent venue at Ingliston in 1960, the Highland Show moved around the country, taking with it all the paraphernalia needed for a major show. This included railway truckloads of sleepers which were used to keep people from sneaking in without payment. During these travels, the show ended up in some less well known locations. Among them were:

1. Berwick – proving its commitment to travel, the Highland Show was twice (1841 and 1854) held in the Pier Park in Berwick on Tweed, these two occasions being the only times the show was held in England. On the first of these events, the organisers pushed the prize money over the £1,000 level for the first time in order to ensure the show was well supported.

2. Inverness – in 1948, the show was held in the Bucht Park in Inverness. This was the first post-war show but it did not attract massive crowds, with only 87,000 coming through the gates. It did however attract royalty, and George VI decreed it should henceforth be called the Royal Highland.

3. Dundee – in 1949 the show was held in the Riverside Park and drew an attendance of 163,917. This record number coming through the gate stood for more than fifty years.

4. Alloa – in 1953, the show made its third appearance in Alloa. A previous visit had the Provost of Alloa describing the show as "one of those little romances that make life interesting". The big interest in 1953 was the main ring demonstration of the Royal Canadian Mounted Police – the Mounties.

5. Paisley – in 1913, the show was held in St James Park which had been favoured over other venues on account of its proximity to two railway stations. The dairy cattle lines were dominated by Ayrshires, with 124 head forward, while British Friesians made their first appearance. The 1913 show also provided the location for local auctioneer William Donald to promote the idea of a Farmers' Union. The idea took off and is now NFU Scotland.

6. Cupar – the show coming to Cupar in 1912 was controversial as some of the directors were not convinced the market town with a population of just over 2,000 had sufficient hotel rooms. A charabanc service to and from St Andrews was organised, but the show was not a success as foot and mouth disease outbreaks curtailed entries.

7. Corstorphine – in 1956, the show was held at Corstorphine on a site to the south of the Maybury roundabout, now under houses, offices and shops. The Duke of Edinburgh, who was show president, made an appearance on the first day.

8. Holyrood – the site of the Scottish Parliament in Edinburgh hosted the first ever Highland Show in 1822. There were 75 fat or very fat cattle forward and the admission fee was one shilling (5 pence).

AFTER THEY WERE NFUS PRESIDENT

Proof there is life after heading up the Union. Presidents follow the lead of earlier holders of the top seat in NFUS, including Sandy Inverarity who went on to chair SAC (now SRUC), and Jim Stobo, who, among other positions, chaired the Scottish Seed Potato Development Council and the Scottish Beef and Lamb Association – now Quality Meat Scotland.

1. Mike Burnett – Union President 1977 to 1979. Governor of Aberdeen College of Education and an Elder and lay preacher.

2. John Cameron CBE – Union President 1979 to 1984. Chairman of Scotrail and member of the British Railways Board, former President of the Scottish Beef Cattle Association and current President of Scottish region of National Sheep Association.

3. Sir Ian Grant – Union President 1984 to 1990. Director of the Clydesdale Bank, NFU Mutual Insurance Society and Scottish and Southern Energy. Chairman of Scottish Tourist Board, Crown Estate, Scottish Exhibition Centre (The Hydro) and Deputy Lord Lieutenant for Perth and Kinross. He is the only former Scottish Union leader to be knighted, but this award was for services to tourism.

4. John Ross CBE – Union President 1991 to 1996. Lord Lieutenant of Wigtown. Chairman of Moredun Research Institute, Scottish Quality Beef and Lamb Association and Dumfries and Galloway Health Board. Director of Quality Meat Scotland and NFU Mutual Insurance Society.

5. Sandy Mole – Union President 1996 to 1997. Chairman of Coastal Grains (in 2001), an 85,000 tonne cereal co-operative in the Borders.

6. George Lyon – Union President 1997 to 1999. One of the first MSPs and Deputy Minister in coalition government. MEP where he used his knowledge of Scottish agriculture to help shape the last review of the CAP. Now on the board of AHDB.

7. Jim Walker CBE – Union President 1999 to 2003. Chairman of Quality Meat Scotland (previously Scottish Quality Beef and Lamb Association) and Managing Director of Motherwell-based biodiesel business Argent Energy.

8. John Kinnaird – Union President 2003 to 2007. Chairman of RSABI, Director of Agriscot and Moredun Research Institute. Deputy Lord Lieutenant of East Lothian.

9. Jim McLaren MBE – Union President 2007 to 2011. Chairman of Quality Meat Scotland, Director of NFU Mutual Insurance Society

10. Nigel Miller – Union President 2011 to 2015. Chairman of Livestock Health Scotland and board member of SRUC.

NUFFIELD SCHOLARSHIPS

Over the past fifty years, more than 1,000 people have been awarded Nuffield Travel Scholarships. Most of these have followed up on mainstream agricultural topics covering livestock and cropping enterprises. A few have taken more esoteric subjects. They include:

1. With Curry the new food of Great Britain, can the Sunday Roast be the new food of Asia? – George E. McK. Finch looked at the possibilities for the meat industry in Asia, focusing on China.

2. Why Build with Straw – Carol Atkinson found through travelling in the US, Canada and Europe that individuals were pioneering this concept on the grounds of sustainability and good insulation.

3. Farming by the Cycles of the Moon – Julian Ellis set out to prove among other things that a waning moon is best for castration or any operation where bleeding could be a problem.

4. Agro-terrorism and Biosecurity; threat, response and industry communication – Richard Byrne studied methods in the US where their experience of planning for large scale disasters has included the need to plan for extreme eventualities into farming.

5. The Future for Insect Biodiversity Products in Poultry Feed – Dr Aiden Leek visited 12 countries and one of his findings was, 'As a fishmeal replacer insect protein has a higher value and will be firstly used in pet and aqua feed before poultry feed'.

6. Earthworm Opportunities for UK Farmers – Fiona Hillman wanted to explore the potential use for earthworms and their casts, and to get behind the hype so often associated with this industry.

7. Alive and Well: Keeping the Balance of Rural Stress – Christine Malseed travelled to Australia and New Zealand to identify best practice in helping to develop existing or new initiatives and projects that would be useful in the UK agricultural industry.

8. How can self-awareness and self-reflection ignite a farmer's motivation to engage in Leadership – Ben Allomes from New Zealand tackled this challenging subject.

9. Advancing Sea Buckthorn – Seth Pasco visited several European countries and the US to learn more about the production, processing and marketing of sea buckthorn; he described the plant as a bona-fide functional food.

10. Driving Profitability through Innovation: Rose Petals for the Culinary Market – Sarah Sammon from Australia travelled to 14 countries and was shown how rose petals can be produced and used for creating speciality foods and nutritional supplements.

A SECOND INCOME

What do you do when the farm or the job doesn't pay well enough? You take a second job. Among others, here is a list of alternative employment that can add to the family income. Be warned though, as climbing up the various greasy poles to get onto this list is extremely difficult.

1. Become a director of NFU Mutual? The largest insurer in the UK's rural scene pays its directors a minimum of £45,000, with a bit more if you also chair one of its sub committees and over £100,000 if you rise to chair the Board.

2. Become President of NFU Scotland? This pays the incumbent £60,000 but do not think that you will be able to do it while still milking cows or growing grain. Keeping the 9,000 or so Union members happy while dealing with all the political problems is no easy task.

3. What about becoming chairman of SAOS? The reward for chairing the co-operative organisation is around £16,000 per annum.

4. Or chairman of SRUC – Scotland's Rural College? The chairman gets £24,500 plus expenses but he/she is expected to spend 30 to 40 days per annum on College business.

5. First Milk director? Remember milk producers can get very, very angry when the price of milk falls at the time when they paid Jim Paice £90,000 per annum to chair the co-operative. This pay was for one day per week as he was also an MP at the time. The milk price plummeted in his two years in the top seat.

6. Rural Affairs Minister? In addition to £60,000 as an MSP, being the Cabinet Secretary in charge of Rural Affairs brings in another £45,000 a year, but do not do this until the problem with the payments computer is sorted out.

7. Chairman of Quality Meat Scotland? The chairman of this meat promotional organisation receives a remuneration of £336.63 per day for a time commitment of 124 days per year.

8. What about becoming a Member of the Scottish Parliament? Quite a number of farmers have taken this route. It does offer over £60,000 per annum, but there are awkward hurdles like elections to get through before taking your seat in Holyrood.

MEEJAH PEOPLE

As rural and urban life drifted apart, farming has had a range of ambassadors to carry the industry's message to those no longer living on the land. This band includes:

1. John Cherrington – started farming in his own right in Hampshire in the 1930s, he was a pioneer of low cost dairying and extensive arable farming. John was a witty and independent writer and broadcaster on farming matters over a 40 year career.

2. Ted Moult – the first farmer/celebrity on television discussion programmes and panel games. He has been credited with the concept of 'Pick Your Own' strawberries at his farm near Ticknall, Derbyshire where he liked to engage with his customers.

3. David Richardson – while in his early 20s he leased a 140ha arable farm with his father, west of Norwich. He was a co-founder of LEAF (Linking Environment and Farming). David is an extensive writer and broadcaster, also leading farm tours to faraway places.

4. Jimmy Dougherty – a Suffolk-based farmer and TV presenter famous for 'Jimmy's Farm' detailing the operation of the Essex Pig Company that he and his wife formed. He now presents a wide range of food-based programmes.

5. Adam Henson – runs the Cotswold Farm Park which his father started and Bemborough Farm, a 650ha arable and livestock unit. He came to fame while presenting on 'Countryfile' but now does a wide range of other TV and publicity work.

6. Matt Baker – brought up on the family farm west of Durham and now lives on a small farm in Hertfordshire. He was a junior British gymnast champion, now one of the main presenters on *Countryfile* and *The One Show*.

7. Nick Nairn – a strong advocate of Scottish produce whether farmed, fished or shot. He is a co-presenter of 'Landward' with Dougie Vipond and has a cooking school at Port of Menteith.

8. John Leese – writer and broadcaster and a passionate promoter of Scottish produced food. He used to plan the National Farmers Union of Scotland annual dinners and many will remember how he enjoyed consuming them.

9. Gregg Wallace – former greengrocer, costermonger, farmer and restaurateur, now a media personality most famous as a judge on *Masterchef*. He also presents a wide range of informative food and farming programmes.

10. The participants in *The Mart* and *This Farming Life* – real farmers and real life, giving a realistic insight to the farming and auction businesses.

11. Kate Humble – presented *Lambing Live* from the Dykes' family farm in Peebles. The whole country now knows how to lamb ewes – and all the problems that can accompany such an event. She has also presented *Back to the Land*.

EXTREME WEATHER

It has been calculated that more than half the conversations between country people start with a comment on the weather. These can range from 'Fine day' which is rare to 'Will this rain never stop' which is quite common. There are many variations in between. The following list highlights the more extreme experiences of the past seventy years.

1. In 1947, after a mild winter deep snow came in March, blocking roads, closing schools and generally disrupting life. Many livestock farmers lost sheep heavy in lamb. A GB-wide Agricultural Disaster Fund was established.

2. In 1963 snow once again closed the country, but this time the Royal Air Force came to the rescue of sheep farmers, carrying out 70 sorties and taking 150 tonnes of feed to hill farms isolated by the heavy snow.

3. In 1967 flooding affected parts of Scotland. In Ross-shire flood banks required extensive re-instatement.

4. In January 1968 gale force winds ripped across the country. Lots of trees keeled over and in the Clyde Valley which was the centre of the glasshouse sector, there was widespread damage. The 'Department' then gave priority to grant schemes for repair work.

5. In both 1975 and 1976 drought affected arable farmers in the east of the country. The two low-yielding potato crops saw a ban imposed on the export of ware potatoes.

6. In 1977, flooding problems across Scotland saw the Government provide grants of up to 70% for flood banks and arterial damage.

7. In 1978, wind again affected hill farmers in the Highlands and Grampian areas where blizzards caused losses of 25% to 50% in sheep flocks in some parts.

8. In 1985 heavy rain during the normal hay and silage making times caused major worries for livestock farmers. Two to three times the normal levels of rain caused dairy farmers to keep their cows inside in July and prevented hay and silage being made. In the arable east, it rained throughout August and September, wrecking the harvest.

9. In 1987 rain again affected farming. This time it was in the North East at harvest time. Eventually the catastrophe resulted in talks with banks, asking them take a sympathetic approach to those affected. It was also the year so-called 'White Settlers' found out why land in the North East was so cheap.

10. In 2015 the poor summer in Orkney and the lack of winter fodder resulted in several boatloads of fodder being sent from the mainland to alleviate the situation. In addition, RSABI helped farmers affected by the disaster.

CHAPTER THREE

SCOTTISH RUGBY PLAYERS WITH A RURAL CONNECTION

Many of Scotland's most illustrious rugby players have been sons of the soil. Among them are:

1. Dave Rollo – played 40 times for Scotland at prop and for the British Lions. He has been a Howe of Fife man as player, coach, and supporter. Dave farmed with his brother Ian on a mixed farm in North Fife.

2. John Jeffrey – played 40 times for Scotland as flanker and for the British Lions: nicknamed the 'White Shark' by media. John's home club is Kelso near where he farms.

3. Ken Smith – farmed on the Roxburgh estate in the Borders. He was capped 18 times for Scotland and played for British Lions, twice against the All Blacks and twice against the Wallabies.

4. Rob Wainwright – a utility back row who gained 37 caps for Scotland, 16 as captain, also playing for the British Lions. His early career was as an army doctor but he and his family moved to the Isle of Coll where they farm and do bed and breakfast.

5. Roger Baird – gained 27 caps for his country. He also played with the British Lions, being selected for four tests and scoring six tries in 11 appearances. Roger is a grain merchant and board member of the Scottish Organic Producers Association.

6. David Sole – played 44 times for Scotland as prop, 25 of those as captain. He was the test loose head prop when the British Lions beat the Wallabies, but the highlight of his rugby career was leading Scotland to a grand slam in the five nations in 1990. David was in the grain trade but is now a management motivator.

7. Jim Aitken – played 24 times for Scotland as a prop and captained his country to a five nations grand slam in 1984. Jim is now owner of one of Scotland's largest grain merchants.

8. Finlay Calder – the archetypal no 7 who had 34 caps for Scotland. He captained the British Lions to a winning series against Australia in 1989. Finlay is a grain merchant who has been heading the establishment of the first distillery in the Borders.

9. Alastair Cranston – played for his country 19 times and was chief executive of the now defunct Border Reivers. He farms in Berwickshire where he was a founder member of the Borders Machinery Ring.

10. Alex Brewster – played for Scotland three times as flanker, three times as prop and captained Scotland on a tour of Japan. Alex and his family have a farming and haulage business in West Lothian.

11. Doddie Weir – gained 61 caps for Scotland and played for the British and Irish Lions in South Africa. He was famously described by Bill McLaren as "On the charge like a mad giraffe". Doddie was brought up on his father's farm in the Borders where he himself bought a small farm on his retiral from rugby.

12. Alex Dunbar – a professional rugby player with Glasgow Warriors. Alex has played 35 times for Scotland, scoring 10 tries. He was born and raised on the family farm near Lockerbie and studied agriculture at Auchincruive.

TOP ALTERNATIVE USES OF BALER TWINE

Apart from its original use, there are infinite ways baler twine can be used on farms. Among those are:

1. When plaited, it can make a livestock halter.

2. Tying up gates around the farm.

3. Holding up the farmer's trousers either as a belt or as braces.

4. Tying up the farm dog.

5. Boot laces.

6. As essential part of nicky tams.

7. As the pull cord on the toilet.

8. As a bracelet for young farmers.

9. Hanging up pictures and prize tickets.

10. Securing tarpaulins on silage pits or straw stacks.

BEST FICTION BOOKS ABOUT FARMING

In addition to all their management text books, farmers and those linked to the industry could to do worse than acquaint themselves with the following. No great husbandry advice, but loads of information on how people think.

1. Lewis Grassic Gibbon: *Sunset Song*
A classic story based in the Howe of the Mearns in the early years of last century. The author had previously worked for the Scottish Farmer.

2. Bruce Chatwin: *On the Black Hill*
Elegantly written homage to the inelegant life of rural Wales, this book is about the lives of twin brothers as they grow up and are shaped by their family and their small community.

3. Gordon Williams: *From Scenes like These*
This novel tells the tragic story of Duncan Logan, a young man growing up in rural Scotland after World War Two. His life is disfigured by violence and drunkenness and he can't find an outlet for his undoubted talents.

4. William Alexander: *Johnny Gibb of Gushetneuk in the Parish of Pyketillim, with Glimpses of the Parish Politics about AD 1843*
Tales of rural Aberdeenshire in Victorian times.

5. David Toulmin: *Blown Seed*
A ruthlessly honest description of north-east farming.

6. Stella Gibbons: *Cold Comfort Farm*
A merciless mickey-take of every rosy glow story about farming ever written. For example, read how Reuben tries to impress the girl by claiming 'I ha' ploughed 200 scrantlets already this morning'.

7. George Elliot: *Adam Bede*
A low-key love story centred round religion, but worth reading for its detailed descriptions of early 1800s farming. Worth the money for Chapter 32 alone, where 'Mrs Poyser Has Her Say Out,' when a tenant farmer's wife reduces the landlord to a nervous wreck.

8. Emile Zola: *The Earth*
There has never been a better description of the bitterness created by family squabbles over small areas of land. Just move the decimal points in hectares involved to take in a family saga near you.

9. John Steinbeck: *Grapes of Wrath*
Dust-bowl America and how the Californian promised land wasn't what it was cracked up to be for itinerant labour.

10. John Nichols: *The Milagro Beanfield War*
The Mexican Americans did the work. The white Americans wielded the power – in this case irrigation – and made the money. But one small farmer diverts the irrigation to what used to be his father's little beanfield.

11. Knut Hamsun: *Growth of the Soil*
Norwegian Nobel prize winner in 1920 writes about the eternal struggle to cultivate the land and make it fertile. Not as gloomy as it sounds.

12. Thomas Hardy: *Far From The Madding Crowd*
Has a lot about an obsessional farmer, a shepherd and helpful hints on how to deal with bloat in sheep.

13. John McNeillie: *Wigtown Ploughman*
A no-holds-barred narrative of a young ploughman growing up in Galloway and which drew attention to the wretched housing conditions of the working farmhands.

COMMENTS NEVER HEARD IN THE FARMHOUSE

The following list was contributed by a farmer's wife. She claims that in more than twenty five years of wedded bliss, she has never heard the following comments…

1. Yes dear, spend as much as you want on that new kitchen.

2. I have put my boiler suit outside as it smelled so I knew it couldn't go in with the school uniform.

3. Let's book a holiday to go away in three months' time. Yes I know that is June, it doesn't matter.

4. Hello, I'm in for my tea. I said five o'clock and it is 4.59. Is that OK?

5. I'll spend the weekend in the garden. That area is just as important as the other 200 hectares.

6. Where are the vacuum/mop/household cleaning supplies? (unless they are needed for the combine or tractor or grain drier)

7. I will be able to come out this evening as that cow that was looking like calving has just done it and there is lots of time to get ready.

8. Let's go shopping. Braehead or Princes Street? Either is good by me.

9. Tight collar and tie? Smart suit/kilt? No bother.

10. Everything today has gone just as I wanted it to.

Tight collar and tie? Smart suit/kilt? No bother.

He said, 'Let's go shopping.'

A ROBOTIC FUTURE

Farming in the early years of the twenty first century is still quite labour intensive. However a view into the near future could see a number of significant savings in the workforce. Developments such as those below are not in the far distant; some are already on farms and the next generation are not far behind. Peek behind the doors of research institutes and machinery manufacturers and you will see white coated boffins working on projects such as these:

1. Milking robots – it has been estimated that almost half of Scotland's dairy cows are now milked automatically and that percentage is rising all the time. Worldwide sales of robotic milking parlours are estimated at almost two billion dollars; a figure that is estimated to quadruple in the next five years.

2. Drones are already in use for field mapping and the technology is being advanced to carry out fertiliser spreading and spraying. Pioneering work is also taking place with drones carrying out planting crops as this will remove problems with soil compaction. As this technology develops, the air will no longer be full of the Sound of Music, instead noises like angry bees from drones doing their business will shatter the silence.

3. Hyperspectral imaging can detect stress in plants long before the symptoms become obvious to even the most experienced eye. The technique uses a high-tech camera with a spectrum of 600 colours. When mounted on a tractor, it can scan crops in the field. As it is more precise than the human eye, it could speed up the plant breeding process by screening out disease susceptible varieties at an early stage. Commercially, hyperspectral imaging on-the-move would allow growers to react quickly to any disease or nutritional threat.

4. Autonomous tractors or tractors without a driver – currently, the use of Global Positioning Satellites (or GPS) allows tractor drivers to chat to their mates or do business as electronics steer them straight as a die down the field, but tractors without cabs for drivers are now being produced. These will be operated remotely on set programmes. The technology will also be used on combines and other harvesting machinery.

5. Sensory weeders – using vision sensors, crop weeding can be carried out. The offending plants will be identified by cameras and then they will be removed by either spot chemical treatment or mechanical means.

6. Centralised use of information – dairy farmers are already using this technology which sends information from sensors on cow's leg tags or collars back to a base where it is then translated into actions the farmer requires to take on animal health or welfare.

7. Autonomous pruners and fruit pickers – these are two labour intensive areas for farmers and therefore a prize target for advanced technology. However, the challenge of getting a robot to tackle the sensitivity needed to pick strawberries or deal with the specialised knowledge needed for pruning remains on the horizon.

TOP TEN BEEF SHORTHORN PRICES

Beef Shorthorn is one of the UK's traditional breeds. It came originally from the North of England but with its hardiness and easy calving ability is now popular in all parts of the country. Its popularity has taken a boost following one of the major retailers paying a bonus for Shorthorn beef. The top prices – in guineas – at auction are:

BULLS

1. 26,000gns for Glenisla Jackpot from Major John Gibb to James Porter, Uppermill in 2017.

2. 17,000gns – Willingham Formalhaut from J. & D. Haigh to Campbell Graham, Aucheneck in 2014.

3. 15,000gns – Chapelton Dauphin from Messrs J. Biggar to B. & J. Landers, Cairnsmore in 2012.

4. 15,000gns – Coldrochie Jurassic from Douglas McMillan to B. & J. Landers, Cairnsmore in 2017.

5. 14,500gns – Pittodrie Upright from R. Laidlaw Smith to Ralph Smith, Sni-a-Bar, USA in 1947.

6. 14,000gns – Pittodrie Uprise from R. Laidlaw Smith to Col. Hardie, Ballathie, also in 1947.

7. 14,000gns – Podehole Beefeater from Harry Horrell to J. Ramsay and M. Moore in 2010.

8. 14,000gns – Jason of Upsall from the Hon G. Turton to G.L. Riby, Stonehills in 2017.

9. 13,000gns – Calrossie Fortitude from Capt. J. MacGillivray to Col. Hardie, Ballathie in 1958.

10. 13,000gns – Chapelton Braveheart from Messrs J. Biggar to Ian Graham, Balgay in 2010.

11. 13,000gns – Podehole Drummer from Harry Horrell to Douglas McMillan, Coldrochie in 2010.

12. 13,000gns – Balgay Gorgoroth from Ian Graham to Campbell Graham, Aucheneck Estate in 2015.

HEIFERS

1. 13,000gns – Chapelton Honeysuckle from Messrs J. Biggar to J. & D. Haigh, Market Rasen in 2012.

2. 11,000gns – Coldrochie Grace Beauty from Douglas McMillan to J.R. Graham & Partners, Biggar in 2016.

MOST WIDELY GROWN SEED POTATO
VARIETIES IN SCOTLAND

For the past century Scotland has had a reputation for growing healthy seed potatoes. Nowadays some £60 million worth are exported to sixty countries around the world. The top varieties are:

1. Hermes 1,656 hectares (ha)
Bred by Saatbah, gives high yields and low tuber numbers. Tubers have high dry matter and good fry colour, making the variety popular for crisping in the UK and overseas.

2. Maris Piper 1,288ha
One of the first varieties bred for resistance to Potato Cyst Nematode (PCN). Bred at the Plant Breeding Institute, Cambridge and still very popular retailed fresh.

3. Desiree 457ha
Bred in the Netherlands by HZPC, it is highly resistant to drought which accounts for its popularity for export to Morocco. It is also still popular for fresh retail in UK with its distinctive red skin.

4. Cara 395ha
Bred by Irish Potato Marketing at Teagasc CRC, Ulster. Very robust variety, PCN resistant and has a wide range of culinary uses. Bulk of seed produced goes to Egypt and Canaries.

5. Markies 303ha
Bred by Agrico UK, this variety has exceptional fry quality with low reducing sugars and good dormancy. Markies has a high tolerance to drought stress and very low requirement for nitrogen.

6. Atlantic 246ha
Bred by the US Department of Agriculture. Suitable for processing into crisps and stands up well to hot climates which is why it is grown mainly for export to Brazil and Saudi Arabia.

7. Pentland Dell 243ha
Bred by the Scottish Crop Research Institute at Pentlandfield, and was one of the first varieties to be bred for mild mosaic resistance. Although originally used in the fresh trade now nearly all used for frozen chips.

8. Valor 216ha
Bred by Caithness Potatoes, the variety gives high yields of bold white tubers with all-round good cooking quality. It is highly adapted to a wide range of growing environments which is why it is a popular export variety.

UP AND DOWN THE FARM ROAD IN THE OLD DAYS

Over the years, the people who have travelled up and down farm roads have changed dramatically. In days gone by they included the following:

1. Tinkers – used to be welcomed on farms at potato picking time when labour was scarce. They were also welcome on berry picking farms and at harvest time. They often erected their tents in nearby woods.

2. Van men – long before farm workers had cars to go to local shops there was a fleet of vans bringing food out to those who worked on the farms. Butchers, bakers, grocers and many other suppliers filled their vans with goods and travelled the country.

3. Local police – part of the community and whether they were checking up on shotgun licences or ensuring sheep were properly dipped, their visits often coincided with a cup of tea round the kitchen table.

4. Irish casual workers – provided hands for singling, potato picking and all other forms of unskilled labour on the farm.

5. Asian salesmen – arrived with large suitcases of women's wear, cushion covers, threads. In the post-war years officially you needed your ration books to buy such things.

6. Grain representatives – came at harvest time with their car boots full of samples. The taking of a sample and its acceptance was no guarantee the load would not be rejected once it was actually at the maltings.

7. Jehovah's Witnesses – they came up the farm road in pairs, these well turned out evangelists and were invariably very polite even in the face of adversity.

8. Farm supply representatives – they could reel off dozens of items you'd never realised you needed and often benefitted from farmers having a weakness for shiny tools.

9. Auctioneers who canvassed for business and spread local gossip.

10. The minister on his bike – more often seen in better weather as he checked up on his parishioners.

11. Men with lorry loads of galvanised gates whose flimsiness was often only found out when faced with a determined bullock.

12. Man offering tarmac at low price because it was surplus to a job he was doing in the area.

13. Ten ton grain lorries with jute sacking covering the leaky wooden sides to prevent spillage.

14. The local hunt – before the fox hunting ban, the hunt was part of the rural scene.

UP AND DOWN THE FARM ROAD NOWADAYS

Having identified those who used to visit farms, the modern-day list is quite different. It includes:

1. Farm assurance inspectors – few farms escape visits from such organisations which help assure consumers about the way food is produced.

2. VAT inspectors – less frequently seen, but more feared. They always seem to have to find something before a look of satisfaction spreads over their faces.

3. 44 tonne lorries – testing the old farm tracks to the limit. Credit must go to most of the operators for their skill in keeping these pantechnicons on what were originally paths for horses.

Giant machinery

Who gives way?

4. Quad bike thieves – they mostly come after dark but more brazen types will soon identify deserted farm buildings and lift anything not locked away.

5. Fuel thieves – a popular pastime for the light fingered and it does not matter if the diesel is red or clear.

6. Hare coursers – more prevalent in some parts of the country where lurchers are kept. Highly illegal.

7. Health & safety inspectors – "Where are the guards" is the panicky cry on days when these people come up the farm road.

8. Boy racers – they tend to see farms as ideal locations for their recreation whether they are on mountain bikes or motocross vehicles. More common near towns.

9. Giant machinery – guaranteed to crush every roadside drain, these monsters – be they tractors, combines, self-propelled foragers or grain drills – tend to fill the whole carriageway, causing any unsuspecting visitor to rapidly back up.

10. White van man – it's not unusual for farms to have two or three white vans appearing each day, whether with Amazon shopping, the agchem delivery or parcels for the non-farming neighbours who know there will always be someone about on the farm to accept their latest delivery.

11. The 'ists' – whether it's the agromonist come to see the farm's crops, or the nutritionist appearing to check on cattle rations, these professional 'ists' seem to be a key part of farms today.

BIBLICAL REFERENCES

"For everything there is a season and a time for every matter under the sun . . . a time to plant and a time to uproot." *Ecclesiastes, Chapter 3* and not Pete Seeger's song 'Turn, turn, turn'. The Bible is full of agricultural references from the very beginning when Adam and Eve were created as people who would farm. Their instructions from God were clear: "To work the land and keep it." This list is as diverse as the Bible itself:

1. The good shepherd who left his ninety nine sheep in safety while he hunted for the one that was lost. *Luke, Chapter 15*

2. The farmer's son who left home with high hopes and full pockets and returned home a humbler man. *Luke, Chapter 15*

3. King Ahab who wanted a vegetable patch next to the palace and was prepared to murder to get it. *1st Kings, Chapter 21*

4. The love story of Ruth and Boaz with its backdrop of the barley harvest. *Ruth, Chapter 2*

5. "Whoever sows sparingly will reap sparingly." The advice of *2nd Corinthians* is to be a cheerful giver and see what happens.

6. Gideon, the mighty warrior who was secretly and with some difficulty, threshing wheat in a wine press. *Judges, Chapter 6*

7. The farmer whose seed fell among stones and thistles on paths to be eaten by the birds and thankfully on good soil too. *Matthew, Chapter 13*

8. The dishonest tenant farmers who are brought to account by the landowner. *Matthew, Chapter 21*

9. Samson who burned the standing grain of the Philistines with the help of three hundred foxes. *Judges, Chapter 15*

10. The wise woman who, in *Proverbs, 31*, assessed the available fields, picked the best, bought it and worked it.

NOTIFIABLE LIVESTOCK DISEASES

One of the big worries of livestock farmers is that their animals may be caught in a clamp down following an outbreak of one of the many notifiable diseases.

1. Anthrax – affects mammals and some species of birds. It was last confirmed in two dead suckler cows in Wiltshire in October 2015. The previous outbreak in livestock in Great Britain was 2006.

2. Avian influenza – or Bird Flu – is a very current problem; a prevention zone announced on 22 February 2017 ran for several months before being removed. Multiple findings in wild birds have been made across the UK since December 2016.

3. Blue tongue – GB is officially a free area, the last outbreak being in 2007. But incursions of new types of the viral disease are causing concern in mainland Europe.

4. Brucellosis – this disease of cattle and other livestock is still present in the EU and Northern Ireland. All of GB has been free since 1985.

5. Foot and mouth disease – is a highly infectious virus disease of cloven hoofed animals. Currently there are no outbreaks in the UK, the last in Scotland being the devastating outbreak in the South and South-west in 2001.

6. Newcastle disease – is a highly contagious viral disease of birds. The most recent outbreak in this country was in the autumn of 2006 in East Lothian.

7. Scrapie – a fatal brain disease of sheep which has been present in the UK flock for more than 250 years. Feeding diseased parts of sheep to cattle was thought to have caused BSE.

8. Bovine tuberculosis – a devastating chronic disease of cattle and a major challenge facing large parts of the UK cattle farming industry. Scotland is officially TB free in recognition of the relatively low and stable incidence of TB found in Scottish herds.

9. Bovine spongiform encephalopathy – Scotland has been free since 2009. BSE is a comparatively new disease of cattle, being first recognised and defined in the UK in November 1986 and made notifiable in 1988. It peaked in the UK in 1992 with over 37,000 head of cattle being infected.

10. Schmallenberg virus – named after a small town in Germany where it was first identified. This virus causes congenital malformation and still births in both cattle and sheep. It first arrived in the UK in 2012.

CHAPTER FOUR

UNUSUAL FRUITS AND OTHER PLANTS GROWN IN SCOTLAND

In their search for something different, growers have been very innovative. Some of their importations and trials include:

1. Cherries – now being grown in polytunnels on a number of soft fruit farms as the demand for fresh fruit grows.

2. Apples – with the rise in cider production and also in farmers' markets, a number of fields of apples have been planted in recent years, but we are still a long way off the 10,000-tree orchard created by Patrick Matthew at Errol in the early years of the nineteenth century.

3. Vines – an attempt is being made to grow grapes outdoors in Fife as the monks did hundreds of years ago. If successful, this would be the first commercial wine production area in Scotland.

4. Blackcurrants – the crop is dominated by Ribena and while the main supplies for this drink come from Herefordshire, there are half a dozen growers in Perth and Angus.

5. Rhubarb – used to be grown on a field scale on the outskirts of big cities. It may never have been popular, but it was cheap and nutritious. In 1913, the census showed there to be 746 acres of rhubarb grown in Scotland. It was also grown close to fruit canning factories as it matured earlier in the season and allowed them to run their production lines.

6. Blueberries – widely recognised as a 'super food' the acreage of this crop has boomed in recent years. Mostly grown in polytunnels to give a long harvesting period.

7. Aronia or chokeberries – grown by several soft fruit growers attracted by their reputation as producing very healthy fruits. Sadly, the fruits are also very, very tart.

8. Honeyberries – a commercial plantation of this soft fruit crop which originates in Japan has been established on the outskirts of Dundee. They are the blue fruits of honeysuckle and they are reputed to be jam-packed with healthy anti-oxidants.

TOP TEXELS

Native to the Texel islands in the north of the Netherlands, the first importation of Texel to this country came in 1973 when 13 Lanarkshire sheep breeders joined forces with the Animal Breeding Research Organisation, Edinburgh to import 27 Texel females and 13 rams from France. Once established in Great Britain, the Texels quickly showed that they were capable of withstanding the rigours of the Scottish winter. The breed is well known in Europe and in Australia, Africa and South America for a quality carcass with a high killing out percentage. The top twelve prices in guineas paid at auction for Texel tups are:

1. 220,000gns, or £231,000 for Deveronvale Perfection from Graham Morrison in 2009, with Jimmy Douglas purchasing. This is believed to be a UK record price for a single sheep but it is not a world record as Merinos with ultra-fine wool have made more cash in Australia.

2. 145,000gns for Knap Vicious Sid from Robert Cockburn in 2014, bought by joint purchasers, C. Boden, K.A. & R. Campbell and Hugh and Alan Blackwood.

3. 130,000gns for Sportsmans a Star from C. Boden in August 2017 to Hugh and Alan Blackwood and John Forsyth.

4. 122,000gns for Tophill Joe from David Houghton in 2003, bought by Messrs Mair, Knox, Forsyth, Lee and M. Lyons.

5. 120,000gns for Loosebeare Imp from B. Quick in 2002, bought by Messrs Forsyth, Lee and Mair.

6. 88,000gns for Claybury Istabraq from J.R. & H.I. Draper in 2002, going to J. Forsyth.

7. 85,000gns for Cornmore Velvet Jacket from John Leitch in 2014, going to John Forsyth and Alasdair Beaton.

8. 70,000gns for Knock Will I Am from Albert and George Howie in 2015, going to Charlie Boden and Mellor Vale.

9. 70,000gns for Teiglum Younggun from Andrew, Alan and David Clark in 2016 to joint buyers Procters Farm and Messrs Boden & Davies.

10. 65,000gns for Forkins Rock Soldi from A. Gault in 2010, going to Trinidad Investments UK.

11. 60,000gns for Teiglum Tornado from Clark Farms, in 2012 going to Robbie Wilson, Messrs Renwick, Allan Chisholm, Donald Rankin and Messrs Vernon.

12. 60,000gns for Clinterty Yuga Khan from Brian Buchan in 2016, going to Gordon Gray, Robert Cockburn, the Wight family, Messrs Gray, Messrs Blackwood, the Knox family, Messrs Arnott and James Currie.

REDUNDANT TOOLS OF THE TRADE

Farming has undergone massive changes since the end of World War II and with each change items that were once invaluable became redundant and consigned to back of the tool shed or even to the coup. Among them are:

1. Sparty rope – made from esparto grass this rough rope was used to tie down stacks and "strae soos". On wet days when no other job could be found, horsemen spent hours rolling sparty into balls ready for use again at the next harvest.

2. 56ers – the 56lb (25 kilo) weights used on the balance scales or steelyards. Too heavy to throw away, they now make handy door stops.

3. Jute sacks – needed for grain and potatoes these came in a range of man-killing sizes. Stored in the couples or rafters these made great homes for mice and rats.

4. Sack needles – used to sew up jute sacks with binder twine, these were easily lost and could never be found when they were needed most.

5. Clats (or hoes) – no self-respecting farm could operate without enough of those to equip a squad of a dozen men, women and children. They were replaced by pre-emergence herbicides for turnips and sugar beet.

6. Tapners – used for harvesting turnips. They had a wooden handle and curved blade terminating with a hooked end. An instrument of torture on a wet or frosty day, these hand tools were used to top and tail the roots in the field. A tapner is still handy for unplugging a choked baler.

7. Berry luggies – the wee buckets tied round a rasp picker's waist – again by binder twine. A lack of sufficient luggies at yoking time could cause insurrection in the field.

8. Bosses – this does not refer to the farmer but they were wooden tripods round which corn stacks and hay coles were built. Not quite a tool perhaps, but still indispensable. Stored in the stackyard out of season these made good wigwams and climbing frames for adventurous bairns to play with. Called Kils in Fife.

9. Stathel stones – large, shaped stones which formed the base of grain stacks, keeping the sheaves off the ground and away from vermin. Now much sought after as garden decorations.

10. Dung graips (forks) – the hard way to empty hundreds of tonnes of well trampled dung out of the cattle courts. The only consolations were that it was a warm job and the ammonia from the dung could clear a cold. Made redundant with the advent of the front-end loader!

11. Chain – not the one that pulls tractors out of muddy holes but the multi-link light chain used to measure fields. Twenty two yards long, it required one person in front putting down markers every chain length and one behind picking them up as they measured the field.

12. Dung hacks – long handled with metal forks at right angles used for pulling dung from the cart and leaving in small heaps to be spread later.

13. Tattie skaips or harps – special multi-pronged graips for loading potatoes into the dresser (mobile grader). Each prong was tipped with a round steel ball to stop it spearing the potatoes. Taking one's turn on the skaip was a good way to avoid hypothermia on a cold morning.

14. Harness – once highly valued, and maintained to perfection, horse harness became redundant as soon as tractors arrived. Eventually most of it ended up in the farm tip. A terrible loss of heritage.

15. Tattie skulls or baskets – much like the berry luggies, an ample supply of these was an absolute pre-requisite for a good day's work. Apart from their main purpose these were handy for the pickers sitting on when the digger was broken. Made of wire mesh or later plastic and holding 10 kilos or more it took a good strong man to lift them and throw them in to the cart without breaking stride.

POLITICIANS GONE BUT NOT FORGOTTEN

Politicians do not go into the job to be popular. The following list contains some of those who had little empathy with the farming community.

1. Fred Peart MP – Minister of Agriculture who was unpopular with Scottish farmers following a measly Price Review in 1965, but he came back for a second spell as UK Agricultural Minister a decade later. Price reviews determined farm incomes in post-war Britain.

2. Nye Bevan MP – Minister of Health in the Atlee Government. He oversaw the introduction of the NHS but didn't endear himself to farmers when he called them 'featherbedded'.

3. Richard Beeching – as chairman of British Rail he produced the 'Beeching Plan' advising scrapping 25% of the rail network in the interests of efficiency. The lines affected included many in outlying areas where transport links were already poor.

4. Margaret Thatcher MP – the 'Green Pound' was a handicap on UK agriculture for its entire lifetime and most of that was during Mrs Thatcher's term as PM. It saw farmers in this country receive less than their European counterparts for their produce.

5. Stephen Dorrell MP – told the House of Commons in 1996 that all the cattle in the UK might have to be slaughtered because of BSE. This threw the industry into a panic and the repercussions are still being felt. Dorrell is now a consultant in the health service.

6. John Gummer MP – Minister of Agriculture in 1996 when BSE was in the headlines. Getting his daughter Cordelia to eat a burger to prove beef was safe did not quell public fears. He is now Lord Deben and sits in the House of Lords.

7. Edwina Currie MP – yet another example of how ill-advised language and exaggeration can cause a major crisis of confidence in a product when she maintained most eggs in the UK carried the salmonella bug. She is now a speaker on cruise ships.

8. Jim Paice MP – former Minister of Agriculture who became chairman of First Milk. He was not popular with dairy farmers for taking a large salary for one day a week's work. One of his announcements was a drop in the milk price when producers were already struggling.

9. Margaret Beckett MP – who throughout her time as Minister for Agriculture held a haughty disdain for farmers. Her main enjoyment outside of politics was caravanning. When not caravanning, she is in the House of Lords as Dame Margaret Beckett.

10. Liz Truss MP – for being invisible during her spell as Minister at Defra. The reward for her silence was promotion to Lord Chief Justice and now Chief Secretary to the Treasury.

BRITISH CHAROLAIS

The British Charolais Cattle Society was the first of the continental cattle beef breed societies to be founded in the UK, in 1962. In France, the breed's home, there are about two million purebred Charolais females, almost all being commercial suckler cows. Within the breed there is a tremendous variation of type, ranging from taller, smoother muscled bulls to heavier double-muscled bulls. Primarily a terminal sire beef breed, it can combine fast growth with good conformation.

TOP BULL PRICES

1. 100,000gns for Vexour Garth from Jan Boomaars and bought by Livestock Capital Partnership at Stirling Bull Sales, October 2012.

2. 70,000gns – Barnsford Ferny from Tom and Sheena Gatherer, sold to Boden & Davies at Stirling in October 2001.

3. 56,000gns – Maerdy Director from Esmor Evans, bought by Wiseton Hall Estates at Perth Bull Sales, October 1989.

4. 55,000gns – Thrunton Voldemort from J.H.C. Campbell & Sons, sold to Esmor Evans and Boden & Davies at Perth, February 2006.

5. 55,000gns – Sportsmans Columbo from Charlie Boden, sold to J.H. Wilson & Sons and Gilbert Crawford at Perth, February 2009.

6. 50,000gns – Balthayock Justice from Major David Walter, sold to J.H. Wilson & Sons and Gilbert Crawford at Stirling, October 2015.

7. 45,000gns – Thrunton Ideal from J.H.C. Campbell & Sons, sold to P.C. Old at Perth Bull Sales, October 1994.

8. 45,000gns – Maerdy Express from Esmor Evans and sold to Boden & Davies, at Stirling in February 2011.

9. 34,000gns – Goldies Uppermost from Hamish Goldie, bought by D. Sawrij in Perth, February 2005.

10. 33,000gns – Balmyle Champion from W.P. Bruce, bought by A.T. Innes at Perth Bull Sales, October 1988.

TRADITIONAL FARMHOUSE DISHES

Before the advent of package holidays, cookery programmes and fast food, most families ate 'slow food' filled with flavour and substance.

1. Scotch broth – a filling and sustaining soup made with pearl barley, onion, carrot leek, turnip and curly kale or parsley. No stock cubes in those days – the flavour came from the piece of boiling beef or mutton cooked along with the rest of the ingredients. Interestingly, kale is now regarded as a 'super food', as is bone broth.

2. Stovies – Sunday lunch was often a roast and the dripping and jelly from the roasting pan were used with onions and potatoes to produce this iconic dish. Extra protein was added in the form of cooked mince, chopped left over roast or cooked sausages. Every family had their favourite variation and everyone's mother made "the best stovies in the world".

3. Skirlie – in the days of cooked breakfasts, this dish was made to add carbohydrate and to make use of the ever-present oatmeal in the farmhouse kitchen. Added to the fat in the frying pan after the bacon cooked this was stirred for a few minutes to absorb the fat (and the flavour). Sometimes chopped onion was added.

4. Baking day meant scones, pancakes, girdle scones or potato scones and of course oatcakes – current dietary advice places these well above bread. The health benefits of including more oats in our diet are well documented. Easy to make and store, they were a staple in many kitchens.

5. Pickled herring – farms near the coast often had a variety of fish in their diet. These herrings were baked with vinegar, onion, spices and bay leaves.

6. Mince and tatties – any extra mouths to feed at short notice could be easily accommodated as there were always plenty of potatoes in the pot and extra stock could be added to the mince. As with stovies, everyone's mother made the best in the world.

7. Clootie dumpling – a mixture similar to, but not as rich as Christmas pudding. The trick was to boil the soft mixture in a floured cloth or 'cloot' until ready and then to remove the cloth, leaving the outer skin intact. The dumpling dried out in the oven or in front of the fire in the old days and was often made in place of birthday cake.

8. Shepherd's pie – traditionally used lamb mince (the clue is in the name) with vegetables and then topped with cooked mashed potato and browned in the oven.

9. Haggis, neeps and tatties – not confined to Burn's night celebrations, haggis is a well-loved Scottish staple. The flavours vary from fairly bland to very spicy. This dish has enjoyed a resurgence through being used by so-called celebrity chefs.

10. Shortbread – another baking day staple and a must for New Year along with Black bun. The home-baked version is unlike the equivalent tartan tin variety.

11. Potted hough – another slowly cooked dish, the end result being shredded beef in a tasty bone jelly. Seldom made at home now but can still be purchased in local butcher's shops.

12. Ox tail – made into a strong and very meaty soup or a slow cooked casserole or stew. Tasty and nutritious as there was a surprising amount of meat on the bones. Ox tails are now available in packs already cut into vertebrae sections, but before pre-packing days when presented with a whole whip-like skinned oxtail the trick was to position a large sharp knife between each section and hit it smartly with the palm of your hand, thus reducing the tail to a range of sections decreasing in size from large (top) to tiny (tip) – not for the faint hearted. Like black pudding and tripe, those who like do, and those who don't, definitely don't!

13. Jugged hare – in the days when hares were seen as fair game, a large hare was a bountiful addition to a frugal diet. They could be made into soup where the main liquid was the blood or made into a superior type of casserole containing red wine. This was known as 'Jugged hare'.

14. Free foods – during both world wars, country dwellers were more self-sufficient, and in the days before supermarkets they were more reliant on home-grown produce as small local shops and travelling vans had limited variety. Most households would produce their own eggs, milk, potatoes, swedes, kitchen garden green vegetables, game of all sorts, chicken, pork and bacon (if a pig was kept, killed and salted down). Use was also made of hedgerow fruits, brambles and sloes and every garden had its rhubarb patch. Interestingly, on the site of an old ruined shepherd's cottage in the Cheviots a flourishing patch of rhubarb has continued to thrive decades after the last inhabitants moved out.

Scotch broth, Shepherd's Pie, Clootie Dumpling,
Shortbread and Scones.

A feast of goodies.

TOP TRACTOR SALES

In 2016, tractors with a combined power of 1.68 million horsepower were sold in the UK market. This was a marginal decrease on the previous year, but the average horsepower per tractor continued to rise, ending up at 158 horsepower per tractor which, as one old horseman commented, "That would need a pretty big stable". Twelve manufacturers accounted for almost all the 11,756 tractors sold in 2016. They were:

1. John Deere – headed the sales list, with 3,159 tractors sold in the UK. The company was established in the 1860s by blacksmith John Deere, whose main line of work was in making ploughs. Most of its tractor production is still based in Waterloo in the State of Iowa.

2. New Holland – originally based in New Holland, Pennsylvania, and now part of the Fiat conglomerate with headquarters in Turin. It also has a tractor plant in Basildon, Essex. Last year it sold 2,126 tractors in the UK.

3. Massey Ferguson – now part of AGCO with its headquarters in Georgia, USA and selling throughout the world, its roots include the former Ferguson and Massey Harris companies. Last year, the company sold 1,377 tractors in this country.

4. Case IH – another multi-national company which has acquired a number of smaller tractor manufacturers since Case and International Harvester came together in the mid 1980s. These include Steiger and East German Fortshritt. The company sold 986 tractors in the UK in 2016.

5. Kubota – a Japanese company which only started making tractors in 1960. Now it has worldwide coverage, selling mainly smaller tractors. Last year it sold 835 units in the UK and was the only one of the top five to increase its sales.

6. Fendt – German tractor and combine manufacturing company which is now part of AGCO. Last year it sold 829 tractors.

7. Claas – another German farm machinery manufacturer. The company makes combines and forage harvesters. Last year it sold 664 tractors.

8. Valtra – Finnish company which is now also part of the AGCO group. Sold 418 tractors in the UK last year.

9. Same Deutz-Fahr – a multi-national company based in Italy. Early SDF companies pioneered using diesel engines and also built the first four-wheel drive tractor. Last year, SDF sold 217 tractors in the UK.

10. JCB – now a multi-national but still family-owned business with 12,000 employees worldwide. It is one of the top three construction machinery companies in the world. Last year it sold 191 tractors in the UK.

NASTY PLANTS

Whether it is injurious weeds or invasive non-native plants, Scottish farmers and gardeners have some tough rules to abide by.

Injurious weeds – it is not an offence to have them on your land. However, you are responsible for controlling them and preventing them from spreading to agricultural land. They include:

1. Common ragwort – the most dangerous injurious weed and the most commonly reported. It is especially dangerous to horses when included in their hay.

2. Spear thistle – occurs widely on lowland and upland grassland and waste places. Large numbers of seeds can be blown across farm and field boundaries.

3. Creeping field thistle – can quickly dominate vegetation in grassland and waste ground, and is often spread by underground root systems.

4. Broad-leaved dock – thrives in high nitrogen environments, open swards and where there is heavy treading by livestock.

5. Curled dock – occurs more commonly on arable and waste land. Both dock species produce many seeds which can remain viable in the soil for decades.

Invasive non-native plants – in Scotland it is illegal to plant any non-native plant in the wild. Among the nasties are:

1. Japanese knotweed – native to East Asia and used in traditional medicine there to treat fungal infections. As a weed it is very difficult to control with its large underground network of roots.

2. Himalayan balsam – a highly invasive annual weed which has spread rapidly through the UK since its introduction in 1839. It chokes riverbank plants and restricts access to rivers.

3. Giant hogweed – its sap is phytotoxic, causing blisters to humans which can lead to long-lasting scars. It was introduced to GB in the 19th century as an ornamental plant.

4. Rhododendrum ponticum – introduced as an ornamental plant in 1760. Its suckering roots and abundant seed produced makes it a severe problem, choking out natural flora.

5. New Zealand pigmy weed – banned from sale in the UK in April 2014. It crowds out other pond growing plants.

SCOTTISH DROVE ROADS

In the days before Codes of Accepted Farm Practice, moving beasts, particularly cattle, around the country required the use of drove roads. Droving generally took place between spring and autumn when there was plenty grazing to be had and when the weather was less inclement. The animals were taken to towns such as Falkirk and Crieff to be sold on. These gatherings were called trysts – not what we would necessarily use the word for now!

1. Bealach na Ba – the infamous Pass of the Cattle on the Applecross peninsula.

2. Kinloch to Crieff – hundreds of cows each year, and as many as 8,000 at one point, made their way from Skye over the Kylerhea – the narrowest point between Skye and the Scottish mainland.

3. Lairig Ghru – the road which leads from Deeside to Strathspey used by drovers and cattle thieves in equal measure.

4. Lairig an Laoigh – lower than its near neighbour the Lairig Ghru, which perhaps explains its name – the Pass of the Calves.

5. Cauldstane Slap – on the Pentland Hills near Edinburgh, this was used by drovers heading for English markets.

6. Poolewe to Muir of Ord – Poolewe was the port of entry for cattle from the isles of Lewis and Harris and a tryst was held at the Muir.

7. Gypsy Glen Drove Road – found near Peebles, Lothian and Borders. As the name would suggest the road wasn't just used by drovers but by travelling people too.

8. Thieves' Road – from Dalwhinnie to Fort William. A drove road across the Highlands. After the Jacobite rising of 1715, in an attempt to eliminate cattle rustling the Black Watch was formed. Despite being based at Dalwhinnie, their attempts to stop the thievery proved unsuccessful.

9. Moniaive to Sanquhar, Dumfries and Galloway – sheep were still being driven up this drove road until the outbreak of World War I.

10. Glen Tilt to Glen Fernate – a Perthshire drove road which led to one of the biggest trysts in the 18th century which took place at Kirkmichael.

CHAPTER FIVE

UNUSUAL CROPS GROWN IN SCOTLAND

Everyone travelling along roads in Scotland will recognise the crops of grain, potatoes and oilseed rape being grown in the fields. However, there are a number of lesser-known crops that either used to be grown, or are only grown on a small acreage. They include:

1. Flax – grown extensively following a deal agreed as part of the 1707 Treaty of the Union. Crops of flax made a brief re-appearance in World War II with a big demand for linen for tents and camouflage.

2. Lentils – almost five million tonnes of lentils are produced annually throughout the world, with Canada being the main producer. Trials are now being carried out in Scotland to see if this important pulse can be grown here.

3. Phacelia – grown as a green crop cover, especially in areas where rabbits are a pest as the little bunnies do not like this plant with its sticky leaves. That is why some farmers sow a strip of phacelia round their fields to keep the rabbits out.

4. Linseed – related to flax, linseed was grown in the 1980s as a result of an EU subsidy being paid for oil seed production. Harvesting often yielded less than the seed used in growing the crop, but as long as an attempt was made to harvest it, the subsidy was paid.

5. Wasabi – a few years ago, trials took place to see if Scotland could grow this nippy Japanese condiment. Despite having plenty of water for growing the crop, the trials were unsuccessful. It is now grown in Hampshire.

6. Tulips – in an effort to find a replacement crop after Scotland's only sugar beet factory closed in 1970, a number of Fife farmers grew tulips on a field scale but their efforts were unsuccessful.

7. Sunflowers – made an appearance in Aberdeenshire a few years ago but have since disappeared, leaving sunflower enthusiasts to travel to Europe where they are widely grown.

8. Mangolds – used to be a popular crop for winter feeding livestock with a big tonnage per acre being able to be grown. Fell out of favour as a result of being difficult to machine harvest.

9. Daffodils – grown on a number of farms in the Howe of the Mearns for both flower production and bulbs. Along with Cornwall, it is one of the main growing areas for this harbinger of spring.

10. Quinoa – this South American staple crop is making a commercial appearance in this country. The quinoa seeds are gluten free and some see it as a super food.

11. Tea – after centuries of importing tea from China, India and Sri Lanka, some entrepreneurs have decided tea bushes can be grown in Scotland's climate. Their innovation is being rewarded by premium prices.

12. Pumpkins – these appear not primarily as a foodstuff but because they are easier to make into lanterns at Halloween. Older people had a much harder time scooping out turnips.

ANOTHER TEN USES OF BALER TWINE

1. Repairing holes in netting, though never quite as effective as the fence it is replacing.

2. As a tag on luggage, even if it gives the game away that you are a teuchter.

3. When a stone is tied on one end, it can be a plumb line.

4. For repairing wooden shafts of hammers, spades and shovels.

5. As an aid at lambing time, especially when dealing with Blackie lambs with horns.

6. Ensuring machinery guards are held in place.

7. As tethers for calves and lambs.

8. As a starting rope for stubborn small engines.

9. Tying up berry bushes.

10. As a replacement bucket handle.

LONG-RUNNING MEMBERS OF THE SCOTCH BEEF CLUB

The Scotch Beef Club was established in 2004 with the aim of promoting the best of beef produced in Scotland. Among the founder members were the following prestigious restaurants:

1. Restaurant Martin Wishart – Martin Wishart was awarded his first Michelin Star in 2001 and for 15 years thereafter. He now has four restaurants including his base in Leith and at Cameron House, Loch Lomond.

2. La Potiniere – found in Gullane, East Lothian, where the owners and award-winning chefs are Mary Runciman and Keith Marley. It advertises traditional seasonal food and gets five star reviews.

3. La Garrigue – in Edinburgh city centre is described as 'an amiable bistro with hearty Languedoc cuisine and French wine'. Jean Michel Gauffre is the chef/owner and much of his food (apart from Scotch Beef) comes from his home region in South West France.

4. The Townhouse Hotel – the Henderson family owns and runs this hotel in the heart of Melrose. Head chef Johnny Streets uses 'the best produce from Scotland's natural larder'.

5. The Galley Rest – in Woodbridge, Suffolk, where international cuisine is prepared in a period restaurant by chef/patron Ugar Vata. Originally from Turkey, Ugar has made this East Coast town his home for over 20 years.

6. Creagan House Restaurant – owned by Gordon and Cherry Gunn who are now in their thirtieth year and proud of their many awards. Cooking is in the modern form, classically French based, using the best quality local produce.

7. The Peat Inn – on the 'Riggin of Fife' won its first Michelin Star in the 80s under chef David Wilson. It is now run by classically trained chef/owner Geoffrey Smeddle who has maintained the high standard and its Michelin star.

8. Kinloch Lodge Hotel – a former 17th century hunting lodge on the Isle of Skye owned by Lady Clare Macdonald. Chef Marcello Tully has won a Michelin star here using classic British ingredients and focussing on local specialities.

9. Isle of Eriskay Hotel – was a 19th century mansion, now a hotel, restaurant and spa. It is a family owned business and a member of the Relais & Chateaux portfolio. The restaurant has a Michelin star and is situated a few miles north of Oban at the mouth of Loch Creran.

10. Deans Let's Eat – in Perth is run by the Deans family. Margo and Willie started the restaurant in 2005. Their son Lee is now general manager and son Jamie, who has trained with Andrew Fairlie at Gleneagles, is head chef. Their aim is 'to provide local, seasonal and exceptional food'.

LARGELY LOST SKILLS

Time moves on, and in its wake it leaves behind skills critical to one generation. Among those on the bonfire are:

1. Building straw stacks – must be a wholly lost skill. Building stacks of sheaves of wheat, oats or barley, each having their distinctive characteristics was carried out by the skilled men only. Together with the ability to build a straw soo of bunches of threshed straw, the art was to build them so that they shed the rain and didn't fall down.

2. Measuring stents or bits – potato lifting time required good mental arithmetic to divide the length of the field by the number of pickers and an element of subterfuge to give the less able pickers half a yard less without the rest of the squad noticing.

3. Pitting potatoes – long rows of potatoes were stored at the edge of the field, one cart-load wide and in a perfect triangle so that the straw bunches which were laid along the sides and then across the top shed the winter rains and kept out the frost. A badly made pit could result in frosted potatoes.

4. Slaughtering and butchering a pig on farm – very few pigs are now kept to eat kitchen waste. Rules on feeding animals human food waste are much stricter now because of foot and mouth disease, and slaughtering rules also preclude farm slaughter and butchering.

5. Singling root crops with a hoe or clat has been eliminated by the sophisticated sowing machines which can put the seeds exactly where they are needed. Swedes was an easier prospect than sugar beet especially before monogerm beet seed arrived. Multigerm seeds were difficult to untangle and could easily be knocked out altogether by a novice.

6. Hand lifting and shawing roots – swedes were pulled then topped and tailed and four rows thrown into one for lifting. Sugar beet and mangolds were pulled and laid out in a double row, tails facing in, then the shaws could be cut off on the ground. The skill was in not cutting off a finger.

7. Drawing a straight furrow – a major skill, especially if the farm was on the roadside and the straightness of a furrow or otherwise could be seen by the neighbours. Now achieved by global positioning satellite.

8. Melling in fence posts by hand while keeping them upright and inline has been superseded by the two-handled post-chapper which envelopes the post or the tractor-mounted hydraulically operated ones.

9. Scything – making roads for the binder or cutting ditch sides of foliage by scythe has been given up by all but good lifers who think they are Poldark. The self-propelled combine harvester made the first task redundant and the strimmer the second. Old timers could make the job look deceptively easy.

10. Hand milking – this once-essential skill for any dairy worker has now been taken over by ever more automatic milking machines.

11. Castrating male lambs – before the near universal use of rubber rings and before animal welfare had a higher prominence, this method was used by some shepherds. The tip of the scrotum was cut off and the testicles gently pulled out with a metal grab or by a shepherd who still had his own teeth.

Hand Milking

'Where is it plugged in?'

MOREDUN'S RESEARCH CONTRIBUTIONS

The Moredun Foundation is one of the largest charities in the UK, supporting livestock health and welfare through research and education. It was set up by farmers in the 1920's and is today still owned and governed by farmers. Many of the vaccines, diagnostic tests and disease control strategies routinely used on farms have either been researched, developed or tested at Moredun. Some of the highlights include:

1. 1920's: Establishment of the Animal Diseases Research Association (now the Moredun Foundation) in 1920 and opening of the Moredun Research Institute in Edinburgh in 1926. Moredun's mobile laboratory conducted field research in Scotland, discovering the causes of many diseases of sheep.

2. 1930's: Development and manufacture of vaccines for braxy (Clostridia) and louping ill (tick transmitted virus) on site at Moredun.

3. 1940's: Moredun scientists discovered the causes of pulpy kidney, lamb dysentery and transmission of scrapie and showed that the agent causing scrapie was very difficult to destroy. Discovery of the use of cobalt to treat 'pine' in sheep and young cattle, and calcium to treat milk fever in cattle.

4. 1950's: Major advances in research into 'kebbing' (enzootic abortion) when a vaccine was developed which halved cases in sheep flocks. A new department of parasitology was opened. Research progressed in various diseases such as scrapie, Johne's disease, pneumonias, Border disease and intestinal parasites.

5. 1960's: Development of disease models and diagnostic tests for Johne's disease; pneumonias in sheep and investigation of a disease causing lung tumours (Jaagsiekte or ovine pulmonary adenocarcinoma). Pasture management for worm control and discovery of Border disease (hairy shakers) in lambs.

6. 1970's: Discovery of protection of lambs and calves against scour using colostral antibodies specific for rotovirus; vaccine development against Pasteurella to prevent pneumonia; immune response against the skin disease orf; anthelmintic dosing strategies to control worms. Opening of the new pathology department and development and manufacture of the improved louping ill vaccine.

7. 1980's: Research focussed on pathogenesis of toxoplasmosis in sheep; treatment for neonatal mortality in lambs involving nutrition in ewes and design of the Moredun warming box to overcome hypothermia; understanding host immune responses to many infectious diseases; Heptavac P (combined clostridia and pasteurella vaccines) and Rotavec

K99 launched. The new biochemistry complex was opened by Her Majesty the Queen. The Equine Grass Sickness Fund was established by the Moredun Foundation.

8. 1990's: Commercial companies established, including Moredun Animal Health (now Moredun Scientific) and Moredun Isolators, with the profit from these companies being gift aided back to the Moredun Foundation. Formation of Pentlands Science Park, the new home of the Moredun Group on the southern outskirts of Edinburgh, officially opened in 1998 by HRH The Princess Royal, the patron of the Moredun Foundation. Toxovax vaccine launched to protect sheep against congenital toxoplasmosis; research into the problems of drug resistance in worm control and new research established on zoonotic, food- and water-borne pathogens and diseases of wildlife.

9. 2000's: Application of new technologies in genetics, bio informatics and host-pathogen interactions to develop new vaccines, diagnostics and disease control strategies. Development of partnerships and collaborations with scientific institutes around the world to progress research and education to prevent and control diseases of livestock worldwide. Broadening of Moredun's research focus to work on sheep, cattle, pigs and poultry.

10. 2010's: Commercialisation of new diagnostic tests against sheep scab and Chlamydia abortus and research to develop an early diagnostic test for Johne's disease in cattle. Launch of Barbervax in Australia, the first vaccine to protect against Barber's Pole Worm (Haemonchus contortus) the most important roundworm parasite of sheep and goats worldwide. Moredun Foundation membership has grown to more than 12,000, the Moredun website has over 200,000 visits per year and the communications team have developed several innovative and award-winning engagement and educational outreach projects.

BEST JOBS ON THE FARM

1. Turning out cattle on to spring grass from their winter quarters and see them delight in careering round the field to check the boundaries before settling down to graze contentedly.

2. Checking the cattle on a sunny summer's morning when their coats are taking on a sheen as a result of the early season grazing.

3. Drilling spring cereals in the best traditions of hope over expectation, sure that the malting barley price will be better than last year.

4. Trial digging potatoes – a never failing buzz of anticipation to find out whether the crop below ground looks as good as what's above ground.

'having that well earned beer after finishing clipping the last ewe'

5. Roguing a crop of high grade seed potatoes in full flower on a dry day without blackleg, virus disease or groundkeepers.

6. The satisfaction of completing feeding, bedding and watering all the lambing pens – everyone looking happy, comfortable and content.

7. After a difficult calving, seeing the cow and calf standing up and feeding.

8. Having that well-earned beer after finishing clipping the last ewe and all fleeces wrapped and put away.

9. When you are picking stones, fed up, back breaking, hating life and your neighbour pops over the fence and asks if you would like a hand.

10. That moment when you realise your lambs have just topped the market.

11. Getting the silage cut and in, the pit tramped and covered without a drop of rain.

12. When your collie dog still loves you after you have had the worst of days and been in a foul mood, she jumps on the back of the bike and give you the biggest snuggle.

WHO TAKES OVER THE FARM?

Generally regarded as one of the main causes of family tension, the issue of 'who takes over the farm' has been analysed by farm business specialist Heather Wildman – and here are her views.

COMMON EXCUSES FOR PUTTING OFF SUCCESSION PLANNING

1. Procrastination, I'll do it tomorrow.

2. Fear of conflict or argument, not wanting to rock the boat or open that can of worms.

3. It's too hard or difficult. It all just seems too daunting or too expensive.

4. I don't know where to begin. It's such a mine field, where do I start?

5. I don't know who to ask, where to get the best advice for me and my family and my business.

6. Bad past experiences, bitter, nasty personal experiences that have left scars, bad feelings and family fall-outs.

7. It's not their job to bring it up… Who's responsibility is it to bring up the topic of succession – you do not want to appear grabbing or greedy.

8. Fear of what is next if they do retire – who will they be or what will they do if they are not 'the farmer/the boss'?

9. Tempting fate, it means death!

COMMON TRIGGERS FOR SUCCESSION PLANNING

1. New members or school leavers joining the business.

2. A family member marries.

3. Starting a new family.

4. Illness in the family.

5. An individual or family member wanting to exit the business or family.

6. High levels of conflict.

7. Communication breakdown.

8. Debt or farm sale.

9. An unhappy or discontented family member.

10. Business expansion and growth.

11. Bank or financial lender insistence.

HOW TO TACKLE SUCCESSION PLANNING

1. Be proactive, take the initiative, start planning now.

2. Maintain a positive attitude.

3. Complete a financial analysis; how is the business performing, is the business viable enough to grow/split/carry another family?

4. Begin with the end in mind – have a clear vision of what you want for your family, your career and your retirement.

5. Read up and become educated on succession, attend seminars, read articles.

6. Use family meetings to open lines of communication. An objective third party can help to ensure that meetings run smoothly and all get to voice their interests and concerns.

7. Think lose-lose mutual compromise and benefit for each family member – there should be no winners and no losers.

8. Generate and discuss various options and learn each other's personal goals.

9. Seek first to understand, then to be understood. Listen to all family members, remain solution focused.

10. Understand that fair does not always mean equal.

11. Create a professional support team who are aligned to your values.

12. Consider tax implications.

13. Act only on sound advice and be prepared to take second or even third opinions.

14. Be the victor, not the victim, by taking ownership, accountability and responsibility. Do not be a victim and blame others.

15. Document your plan.

EVOCATIVE ODOURS OF THE COUNTRYSIDE

Some people go into raptures over the smells of the countryside, others do not. Below are some that divide the nation:

1. Oilseed rape flowers – bit of a Marmite one this. Some people love it, hay fever sufferers hate it, but there is no denying it is distinctive and on a warm sunny day can be strong and pervasive.

2. Potato flowers – some varieties flower more than others and some seem to have more scent than others, but the ability to tell varieties apart by the flower scent, claimed by some, is open to doubt.

3. Middened dung – when spread on a crisp winter's day it has an attractive smell to many a countryman's nose. This is not to be confused with dung, fresh from the courts which has a strong but less attractive odour, and the less said about slurry, poultry or pig dung the better.

4. New mown grass and well-made hay have an attractive summer smell, each evoking a seasonal connection.

5. Silage which is well-made has an attractive, slightly vinegary smell and it is not surprising that livestock lap it up while turning their noses up at the overcooked smell of silage that has been allowed to overheat.

6. Soil freshly turned over by the plough has an earthy, slightly savoury smell. Is it the decomposing humus? Petrichor is the name of the scent when rain falls on dry soil and releases bacteria into the air.

7. Harvested barley as it flows out of the combine or out of the trailer has a distinctive, sharp smell, a welcome smell, unlike the smell of overheating barley which has been harvested while not dry enough.

8. Day-old turkey chicks on fresh shavings under a heat lamp – the only day in their lives when turkeys are in any way attractive.

9. Smoke – wood smoke of any kind conjures images of an open fireside on a winter's day. Straw smoke from burning straw bouts is a distinctive autumnal smell, but it can also remind less careful straw burners of the time when a burn got out of control. A burning heap of paper grain-seed bags as the last act of drilling a field gives out a distinctive smell due, we are told, to the salt-petre in the bag.

10. Freshly sheared fleece – smelling strongly of lanolin is attractive at that stage of the wool's life but is unwanted by the end user and is eliminated in the process from sheep to shop.

HIGHLAND CATTLE

Whether they are seen on a bleak mountainous countryside or pictured on a tartan-clad box of shortbread, Highland cattle are easily the most recognised cattle breed in the country. And they are not only popular in Scotland, as the list of top prices at auctions shows that Highlanders are in demand in a number of countries:

Coming in at joint number one are:
Jock of Pennygown, sold at the Oban February sale 1992 for 20,000 guineas (gns), bred by Donald McGillivray, Pennygown Farm, Isle of Mull. Bought by K.W. Walker, Leys Castle, Inverness.

Seumas of Pennygown, sold at the Perth Highland sale February 1994 for 20,000gns, from the same breeder as Jock (above). Bought by Alma SA, Azienda Agricold Bioldgica, Switzerland.

Followed by:
Rushmore Bracken, sold at the Oban February sale 1992 for 18,000gns, bred by Robert Montague, Pusey Estate, Oxfordshire. Bought by Peter Waterman, Black Jane Farm, Cheshire.

We have three contending for fourth spot:
Victor of Earn, sold at the Oban February sale 1989 for 14,000gns, bred by Heather Corrigall, Nigg, Easter Ross. Bought by Leon van Tongern, the Austie Fold, The Netherlands.

Valentine of Benmore, sold at the Perth Highland sale February 1994 for 14,000gns, bred by Judy Bowser, Auchlyne Farm, Killin, Perthshire. Bought by Dunbeath Estate, Caithness.

Lasgaire of Roisbheinn, sold at the Oban February sale 2008 for 14,000gns, bred by Alan and Mary-Ann Blackburn, Roisbheinn Farm, Loch Ailort, Inverness-shire. Bought by Herr Falko Steinberg, Lehstener Moor Fold, Germany.

Taking seventh position is:
Islay of Upper Cornabus, sold at the Oban February sale 2004 for 12,000gns, bred by J.J. Monaghan, Upper Cornabus Farm, Port Ellen, Isle of Islay. Bought by S.K. Brown, Brownhaze Fold, Wiltshire.

In eighth place is:
MacAlaster of Coirefuer, sold at the Oban February sale 1992 for 11,000gns, bred by Angus Mackay, Coirefuar Fold, Loch Lomond. Bought by Ewan A. Cameron, Glen Nevis, Fort William.

THE KELSO RAM SALES

The second Friday in September sees thousands of sheep farmers from all over the UK and Ireland converge on the small town of Kelso in the Scottish Borders for the oldest and still one of the biggest ram sales in the country. Notable facts about the sale include:

1. The first sale was held on 12 September 1838, with 120 Border Leicester rams forward for sale. This was probably the first ever public auction of sheep in the country and three auctioneers sold the rams at between £3 and £4.

2. Jim Clark, the world champion racing driver and Borders farmer used to sell his tups at the sale in the 1960s from his farm at Edrington Mains.

3. The railways came to Kelso in the early 1850s and transformed the sale from a local event into a national one. Entries surged to more than 1,500 by the middle of the decade, all of them Leicesters.

4. Springwood Park – after outgrowing the original site, the sale first of all moved to Springwood Park in 1870, but it only became its permanent site in 1943. The site was bought by the Border Union in 1953 for £5,500. It has also hosted the Highland Show on a number of occasions. The last time the show came to Kelso was in 1952, little more than a decade before it settled down at Ingliston.

5. Early 'other breeds' – the first to break the monopoly of the Leicester breed at Kelso were Half Breds who were entered in 1864. Shropshire Downs were then entered for the 1877 event.

6. Auctioneers – although they are now sheltered from the elements, auctioneers have had to battle with driving rain and wind in their selling stint. Some of the selling efforts have been Herculean, with one of the original auctioneers, Fairbairn of Kelso, selling up to 800 tups in a nine-hour session without a single break.

7. Tup taxis – since 2000, one sight at Kelso tup sales are the quad bikes with small trailers taking tups that have been sold to the livestock lorries at the park's edge.

8. Suffolks – the first Suffolk tups were sold in 1892, but by the middle of the twentieth century, this breed, noted as a terminal sire, dominated the sale. They were toppled from this podium in 2004 when Texels became the main breed.

9. Rings – in 1992, no fewer than 19 rings were in operation, this number having gradually increased over the years as the sales confirmed their place in the UK sheep industry.

10. Record price – the top price at Kelso is £35,000 for a Texel from P. & L. Gray, Scrogtonhead, selling to Proctors Farm, Lancashire.

ONCE COMMON NOW BANNED CHEMICALS

Many of the pesticides which were introduced last century had long persistence on the target species but this once desirable characteristic, which makes them less environmentally friendly, has seen them banned.

1. Gramoxone was the trade name for paraquat and was banned in the EU in 2007. It was a valuable pre-emergence weedkiller, killing off all green growth but de-activated once it hit the soil. A number of tragic cases resulted from accidental intake of the concentrate.

2. Dinoseb herbicide was widely used for post-emergence weed control in cereals and a wide variety of other crops. It was a nasty chemical to use and was highly toxic to mammals.

3. Simazine was banned by the EU in 2016 after fears about links to infertility, reproduction and foetal development. It was used to control broad-leaved weeds and annual grasses in a wide variety of crops.

4. DDT is an organochlorine insecticide initially used during World War II to control malaria and typhus, but its persistence in the food chain led to its ban some 50 years ago. There is still an ongoing debate, however, as to whether its use would be the lesser of two evils in controlling mosquitoes and thus malaria in Africa.

5. Sulphuric acid is now mainly used in fertiliser manufacture. It was once widely used as a desiccant, burning down potato haulms and was favoured because of its quick action, but was banned because of user safety and danger to animals running through treated crops.

6. Bordeaux mixture is a copper/sulphur mix and was used to prevent late blight in potato crops. Its use has been superseded by more effective chemicals with commercial growers, but it was used by gardeners and organic growers until its ban in 2014.

7. Strychnine was used to control moles but has been banned since 2006. When mixed with earthworms and placed in the moles' tunnels it was a very useful method of control.

8. Cypermethrin was an organophosphate sheep dip and a very effective and persistent method of controlling parasites on sheep's skin and in their wool. It was banned at the end of last century because of issues about user safety and persistence in the environment.

9. Elvaron was the most widely used trade name for dichlofluanid, one of the earliest (introduced in 1965) and most effective fungicides for preventing botrytris on fruit and vegetables; it was also used as a wood preservative.

10. Derris once was the recommended treatment for cattle suffering from warble fly larvae. It had to be mixed in a bucket and scrubbed along cattle's backs. Pour-on Ivermectin is easier to administer and, being systemic, is preventative as well.

CHAPTER SIX

MOST ESSENTIAL CONTENTS OF TRACTOR TOOLBOX

The items below relate to the tractors which were common in the second half of last century and not to the behemoths seen today which need an electronics engineer when they break down.

1. Hammer (ball-peen) – essential for all acts of persuasion, whether it is a stone stuck in a web or a reluctant pin on a bogie side.

2. Cold chisel – used in conjunction with the above to cut off nuts and bolts which won't yield to a spanner.

3. Screwdriver (robust) – as well as the usual function of engaging with a screw nail or bolt it has been used with the aforesaid hammer to remove stones from tricky places.

4. Pliers – cutting wire and securing the head of a bolt while tightening the nut.

5. Adjustable spanner – although not as efficient as the correct spanner for the nut size, the adjustable, as the name suggests, is flexible and handy for minor repairs.

6. Vice-grips – as with the adjustable, vice-grips' flexibility make them an essential addition to the tractor toolbox where space was at a premium.

7. Fergie spanner – one and one sixteenth of an inch at one end and eleven sixteenth at the other and marked off in inches and centimetres, it was designed to fit most of the nuts on the early Fergies. Although useful as a fuel tank dip or measuring ploughing depth it often failed when the nut needing attention was the wrong size.

ESSENTIAL ITEMS IN A FARM WORKSHOP

1. Vice – whichever job is being tackled it is always essential that the item under attack is held firmly to avoid staved fingers or worse.

2. Angle grinder and drill – easier, quicker and more efficient than a hacksaw and a brace and bit.

3. Socket set and spanners – essential items in most farm workshops but their effectiveness is increased if they are always put back in their proper place.

4. Claw hammer and saw – for all wood related jobs.

5. Heavy hammer and anvil – where a bit more than gentle persuasion is required.

6. Workbench – substantial and well lit.

7. Jump leads and battery charger – to avoid the first use the second.

8. Welder – whether this is an electric welder or oxy-acetylene, small welding jobs can save an expensive trip to the blacksmiths.

9. Grease gun – with flexible hose, housing a grease cartridge. Handy for inaccessible parts of large machinery like combines but were a nightmare to refill.

USEFUL DORIC FARMING WORDS

If you've ever met a Buchan farmer and struggled to understand their broad Doric dialect, the following list might just help…

1. Heid bummer – the top person, boss or leader – like the president of NFU Scotland.

2. Nowt – nothing to do with 'nothing', this is the Doric word for cattle, one of the most important parts of farming in Buchan.

3. Baillie – another word which can be confusing. Doesn't bear any relation to managing river fishing, but all to do with managing the aforementioned nowt.

4. Cushie doo – a pigeon, the sworn enemy of anyone trying to grow a crop, especially if the weather has been bad and it has brackled.

5. Gushet neuk – the corner of a field, and almost always where pigeons (and crows) seem to be most active when things go wrong with a crop, and always closest to the road in that case.

6. Tyaavin awa – working away at something. Almost always used when things are a bit of a struggle, and when they're really bad, it is bound to be a 'sair tyaav'.

7. Forfochen – when it has been a 'sair tyaav' all day, you'll be 'fair forfochen', or just exhausted.

8. Lowsin time – when it's all too much, you are 'fair forfochen' and it is time to go home.

9. Styoo – the dust that gets up on a dry, windy day.

10. Dubbs – what becomes of the dust after rain – ie mud.

11. Sharn – what's left on you if you stand too close to a defecating cow.

12. Redd up – a mess, and sometimes can be used to say you are tidying up. Messy steadings can sometimes be a 'redd up'.

13. Mochy – the sort of muggy weather which helps spread potato blight like wildfire.

14. Dingin doon – heavy rain or snow. Never good.

15. Knapdarlach – the bits which always end up clinging to cattle tails – no need to spell out what they're actually comprised of…

FORMER YOUNG FARMERS COMPETITIONS

The Romans had a saying "Times change and we change with them". The proof of that proverb holds true today when some of the Young Farmers competitions from a previous era are considered. They include:

1. Poultry trussing, which used to be an integral part of the girls' competitions at the Highland show.

2. Pinta Princess – popular in the 1970s, but in these more politically-correct days, this competition has been consigned to history.

3. Miss Scotch Lamb – see above. This was promoted by the Scotch Quality Beef and Lamb Association, the predecessor to Quality Meat Scotland.

4. Miss Dairy Princess – also see above. This was run in conjunction with the Scottish Dairy Show in Glasgow.

5. Thinning roots – popular in the pre-precision sowing era. The competition allowed either the use of a hoe or it could be done by hand.

6. Identification – whether they were weeds, seeds, or bit of machines, you had to know what they were.

7. Tossing the sheaf over the bar – being able to throw a sheaf of straw was an essential skill in making a straw stack. Nowadays no stacks are built, no sheaves are made and no pitchforks are left.

8. Fertiliser distribution – one of the SAYFC proficiency tests in the 1970s before the arrival of electronic gadgetry.

9. Building a straw stack – in the early twentieth century, this was a real and treasured skill, and you could still sit a Young Farmers proficiency test in stack building in the mid-1970s.

COUNTRYSIDE EYESORES

Beauty is definitely in the eye of the beholder and some may like the following range of suggested 'eyesores'.

1. Poly-tunnels – don't contribute anything to the beauty of the countryside, but are the price we pay to have unblemished soft fruit from May till September in Scotland.

2. Insect mesh – used to cover swedes, protecting them from turnip flea beetle and avoiding the use of insecticide sprays. But it is on fields from spring until harvest in late autumn and it does harbour large unsightly weeds.

3. Fleece or polythene plant covers – used to cover vegetable and potato crops to prevent soil blow, protect from frost and cold and to speed up plant growth. Their saving grace is only being on crops for a few months in spring.

4. Discarded polythene – whether in the form of sacks or silage covers, it is often carelessly discarded, with farmers and their employees being the culprits. Particularly unsightly when the torn scraps (witch's knickers) are caught in roadside hedges.

5. White tape – this electrified tape is used round some horse paddocks and is probably an effective means of containment. It becomes an eyesore, however, when it is left round a field in big slack loops obviously unpowered.

6. Abandoned broiler houses – and other specialised buildings should (some think) have had a planning condition when built to force owners to remove them when not used for their original purpose.

7. Fallow fields – and parts of fields are in this condition because of EU rules on 'greening'. The weeds which grow unrestrained may be of benefit to partridges and skylarks, but these eyesores detract from some people's view of what a well-managed countryside should look like.

8. Litter – comes in at least two forms, firstly 'fly tipping' by the unscrupulous end of the 'white van man' community, and secondly rubbish thrown out of vehicle windows by those too stupid, selfish or lazy to take it home. As the law stands, whoever's property it lands on is responsible for its removal.

9. Stackyards which resemble scrapyards – tens of thousands of pounds-worth of machinery can lie rusting quietly in the long grass on many farms.

10. Dog dirt – dog owners may think they are clearing up after their pets by putting the faeces in little black bags but if they sling the bags over the fence, they often end up hanging from the branches of trees like particularly unpleasant Christmas decorations.

Dog dirt.

'Is this where we leave the poo bags?'

WORLD CHAMPION FARMER CURLERS

Curling or the roaring game was enjoyed by farmers and landowners in the long cold winters before global warming put an end to it being played on lochs and ponds. Now in modern arenas, the game is much more skilful and takes its place in the Winter Olympics.

1. Chuck Hay MBE skipped the Scottish team which won the 1967 World Curling Championships, known then as the Scotch Cup. Chuck farmed at Easter Rhynd where the Tay and Earn join and his home club was Kilgraston and Moncrieffe.

2. John Bryden was Chuck's third player in the 1967 Scotch Cup win and his home club was Fingask. John farmed and had a potato merchant business at West Mains in the Carse of Gowrie.

3. Alan Glen was second player in the Championship winning rink. His home club was Glendoick, not far from where he farmed at Mains of Errol.

4. David Howie lead in 1967. His club was also Glendoick and he farmed at North Murie, also in the Carse. All three of Chuck's rink lived and worked in the Carse of Gowrie with Chuck himself just over the Tay from them.

5. David Smith was skip the next time Scotland won a world men's title in 1991. He and his rink beat Canada in the final in Winnipeg. David farms at Hallroom near Guildtown just north of Perth and commentates on TV at world championship curling events.

6. Peter Smith played second to his brother in 1991, but went on to win two further golds in 2006 and 2009 with David Murdoch. After many years working on the family farm, he is now commercial director UK and Ireland with Yara UK.

7. David Hay, Chuck's eldest son, was in David Smith's rink in 1991. His career has included winning many other national and European titles. David's club is Dunning and he oversees an extensive farming operation with its base at Easter Rhynd.

8. David Murdoch skipped the winning rink for Scotland at the 2006 and 2009 World Championships and represented Great Britain at three Winter Olympics, culminating in a silver medal at Sochi in 2014. Brought up on the mixed family farm near Lockerbie, he has been a professional curler for most of his adult life.

9. Euan Byres played lead for David Murdoch, being part of the team to win two world golds and Olympic silver. He is a dairy farmer at Cleuchside, Castlemilk, Lockerbie.

10. Gordon Muirhead, alternate in 1999 for Hammy McMillan's world championship team, and father of ladies' world champion skip, Eve. Gordon farms with his two sons, Glen and Thomas, at Blair Atholl, Perthshire.

POPULAR TREES

MOST WIDESPREAD TREE SPECIES IN SCOTLAND

Scotland is well known for producing barley (340,000ha) wheat (87,000ha), oilseed rape (34,000ha), oats (32,000ha), and potatoes (29,000ha). But Scotland grows almost as big an area of Larch as it does potatoes, although the Phythoptera which is currently blighting the Larch crop receives far less attention and research than that more famous Phythoptera, potato blight, has done over the years.

SCOTLAND'S TOP TREE SPECIES BY AREA

1. Sitka spruce – 229,000 hectares
2. Lodgepole pine – 52,100 hectares
3. Scots pine – 45,000 hectares
4. Larch – 26,400 hectares
5. Norway spruce – 10,900 hectares
6. Birch – 9,200 hectares
7. Douglas fir – 5,400 hectares
8. Oak – 2,500 hectares
9. Beech – 600 hectares
10. Alder – 600 hectares

WITH SITKA SPRUCE TOPPING THE LIST
HERE ARE TEN USES OF THE SPECIES

Scotland's most popular timber tree, the spiky Sitka, is sometimes assumed to be a commoner with little special about it. On the contrary, its versatility and quality is what helps make it so popular. Here are just a few of its many uses:

1. Timber frame houses.
2. Ship building and boat construction.
3. Sitka has excellent acoustic properties, so is used for sounding boards in pianos and to make violins and guitars.
4. Its high ratio of strength to lightness made it the favourite wood for aircraft construction.
5. Pallets.
6. Fence posts.
7. The young shoots of new growth are rich in vitamin C and can be made into tea or syrup.
8. The white colour of the wood and long cellulose fibres make spruce thinnings particularly valuable for paper making.
9. First Nation people in north-west America used native Sitka spruce roots to weave water-tight hats and baskets, ropes, fishing lines and twine.
10. Pitch made from the tree can be used to caulk boats or waterproof boxes.

TOP TEN SAOS MEMBERS TRADING IN SCOTLAND

SAOS, the umbrella organisation for farm co-ops in Scotland was established in 1905 and is a co-op, owned by farmers' co-ops. Apart from developing, delivering and supporting co-operation and collaboration in farming and food and drink supply chains, it also involves local food development and co-ordinates research and development of data systems for Scottish Government. It is seen as a critical driver for Scottish agriculture in becoming smarter, more efficient, more resilient and more innovative. The top ten SAOS members trading in Scotland, by turnover/throughput, are:

1. £710million, Openfield Agriculture – a grain co-operative based in Lincolnshire and one of the UK's leading grain exporters. It is a key supplier for many of the biggest brands in the country, including Warburtons.

2. £294m, First Milk – the only major dairy company owned by British farmers. The co-op's head office is in Glasgow and its members stretch from Kintyre to the South of England and west Wales to East Anglia.

3. £268m, United Oilseeds – has 4,500 member owners and a board of farmers from across the UK. The co-op is Britain's only specialist rapeseed marketing company.

4. £153m, GrainCo – provides cereal marketing services for 2,000 farmers in the North East of Scotland, the Borders and northern England.

5. £124m, ANM Group – established in 1872 and now one of the largest and most progressive producer-owned farming, food and finance businesses in Scotland.

6. £92m, United Farmers – a 'federal' co-op based in Edinburgh. As a federal of co-ops, it maximises the collective purchasing power of its 25 member co-ops and farm supply businesses in securing farm inputs.

7. £56m, Tarff Valley – established in 1903 by tenant farmers to buy supplies. It now has 1,000 members and a string of Tarff Town & Country stores across South West Scotland and northern England.

8. £52m, Scottish Pig Producers – markets pigs for its 110 members in Scotland and Northern Ireland. It worked closely with co-ops Scotlean Pigs (below) and Tulip to redevelop the Brechin abattoir and secure vital processing for Scottish pigmeat.

9. £50m, Scotlean Pigs – a marketing co-op with 95 members. It markets pigs into the most logistically suitable and profitable outlets for producer members.

10. £34m, Ringlink (Scotland) – Scotland's largest machinery ring, which co-ordinates machinery and labour between its 2,800 members and also supplies a host of commodities and services.

Agricultural co-operation provides a host of benefits, including:

• More competitive farming – neighbouring, sharing, group farming, machinery rings, advisory groups, animal health groups, innovation and new ventures.

• Supply chain participation and collaboration – buying groups, supply co-ops, marketing groups, central grading, packing, quality control and processing.

• Strategic strength in UK production, food manufacturing and processing or marketing.

• Machinery and labour ring co-ops provide a wide range of cross-contracting and group services provided via a low cost transactional platform.

POPULAR FARMER GAMBITS

Farmers are usually canny negotiators, with some well-honed negotiation skills:

1. "HOW much" – usually when faced with an opening price for an expensive piece of machinery.

2. "No, no you'll have to do much better than that. I'll get a quote from another firm."

3. "Can you let me have it on demonstration" – could last long enough.

4. "I'll need to check with the boss/partner/wife" – a good stalling practice which allows for thinking time.

5. "But what is your real price" – can be used with "what's your margin? Let's negotiate".

6. "The best I can do is" – and like all bargaining start low enough to allow face saving on both sides.

7. "You know I've been a good customer for donkeys' years, so I'm trusting you to look after me" – really pulling at the heart strings here.

8. "And how much for cash" – note to any HMRC moles this is a purely fictional gambit.

ALTERNATIVE LAND USES

There are other ways to make a living from the land than selling cattle and sheep or barley and potatoes. Below is a list of some of the options and some of the caveats that come with them:

1. Caravan parks – for those farms near the coast or another tourist attraction, the opportunity to turn a field into a caravan site will see the field yield more than a barley crop. Acceptable when properly screened.

2. Solar panels – even with subsidies for renewables much reduced there still seems to be an economic case for their construction. An option in the sunnier parts of the country and acceptable in the right location.

3. Wildlife sanctuary – not sure that the option of turning over part of a holding for the exclusive use of wildlife will yield much in direct income, but those inclined don't take this step purely out of altruism.

4. Wind turbines and telephone masts – a nice little earner whether owned or let to an energy company and they don't take up too much land. One would have to be prepared for some resistance to the idea from neighbours however.

5. Golf courses – we are told this country is now at saturation point, so a once profitable alternative use for poorer seaside sandy soils now seems to have dried up.

6. Horse riding cross-country courses – the more varied landscape and contour the better for making an interesting course, but probably has to be considered in conjunction with other horse activity.

7. Children's adventure playgrounds – well run, well equipped layouts are well attended, but most will be built as part of a farm shop and the obligatory café/restaurant.

8. Development – for housing, industry or car-parks will be the most lucrative alternative land use. Needless to say, it only applies to those bordering towns and is also irreversible.

9. Sand and gravel quarrying – where the underling glacial deposit is suitable this will be an option for some, provided the disruption during extraction can be tholed. And the land will be as productive as ever once the soil is returned.

10. And as traditional cemeteries fill up, there is a demand for **rural burial plots**. Provided they are in a beautiful, tranquil location, people just die to be buried there…

Wind Turbines & Telephone Masts

Money Spinner.

UNUSUAL POTATO FACTS

1. Chelsea Flower Show and The Potato Story

In 2017, Morrice and Ann Innes from Newmachar near Aberdeen made it a hat trick of gold medals for exhibiting potatoes at the Chelsea Flower Show. The display consisted of 150 varieties, part of Morrice's 500 variety-strong collection. The Potato Story had global appeal on social media, and even the Queen making an unscheduled stop for 'tattie talk' in 2016.

2. The Lumpers famine of 1845/46

With a growing population in the late 18th and early 19th century, the potato was a staple food, with over-dependence on it, particularly in the West of Scotland. Varieties tended to have a short life span as they succumbed to 'the curl' virus, so new varieties were in demand. One of these, Lumpers, was introduced in 1805 and rapidly were adopted for its high yield and keeping qualities. However, when the first potato blight spores appeared, they found no resistance in this single variety and decimated the crop in a matter of days. The result was hunger, a flow of people to the central belt and emigration to Canada. It also led to a new era of potato breeding, with Scotland being the leader.

3. Eldorado, the £250,000/t potato

In 1904, the Strathearn Herald reported: "Mr J.L. Anderson, town clerk, Cupar, sold on Tuesday a single Eldorado potato for £30 to a well-known Scotch firm of potato merchants dealing in new varieties and who were acting on behalf of an English customer. The potato weighed slightly under four ounces and the price thus works out at nearly £10 per ounce and considerably over quarter of a million per ton." The breeder was Archibald Findlay of Auchtermuchty who also bred the variety Majestic.

4. Donald Mackelvie, the man behind the Arran potato varieties

Accountant Donald Mackelvie (1867-1947) returned to the Island of Arran to run his uncle's store. He started breeding Highland ponies and then moved on to potatoes. His best-known variety, Arran Pilot (so named as his uncle was a river pilot on the Clyde), was a national favourite for 30 years and is still going strong with gardeners. Another, Arran Banner, saw the seed exported to Cyprus and the local newspaper is named after it. Arran Victory, so named to commemorate World War I, is still a favourite with gourmet chefs. The not so well known Arran Cairn was used in the crossing programme to produce Maris Piper.

5. The first potato field in Scotland

According to parish records, Robert Graham, occupier of Tramrawer Farm, Auchincloch, near High Banton, Bonnyrigg, was the first to introduce the potato as a field crop, in 1762. This gave a yield of "twelve fold from planting of one tuber". The locals firmly believe this is the first commercial field of potatoes in Scotland.

6. The start of Ayrshire early potatoes

In 1865, Quinton Dunlop of Morriston Farm and Mr Hannah of Girvan Mains visited the Channel Islands to study the production of early potatoes. Returning home, Mr Dunlop thought his farm and proximity to the coast were ideal. For fertiliser, he hired barges to meet the overnight Irish cattle boats and offload their unwanted cargo of dung. The recently built Maybole train line also solved his second problem – getting the crop to market in Glasgow.

7. Scotland's only crisp producer

In 2009, the Taylor family from Moncur Farm near Dundee joined forces with Mackie's from Aberdeen to produce Mackie's Crisps, now made on the site of the Old Errol Brickworks. Following the closure of Golden Wonder's Broxburn factory, then Highlander crisps, Mackie's is the sole Scottish crisp producer. Its lines have a truly distinctive Scottish theme with Flame Grilled Aberdeen Angus, Haggis and Cracked Black Pepper, and for the brave, Scotch Bonnet and Chilli Pepper.

8. The Pentland Alphabet

The Scottish potato breeding programme to tackle blight susceptibility followed the letters of the alphabet in its naming convention. Pentland Ace in 1951 was followed by Beauty, Crown, Dell, Envoy, Falcon, Glory, Hawk, Ivory, Javelin, Kappa, Lustre, Meteor and Marble. There were no Pentland varieties beginning with N, O, P, or Q, but Raven and Squire followed in 1970. After the UK joined the Common Market no more breeder prefixes were allowed.

9. The Mother of Modern Potatoes

William Paterson (1810-1870) from Seafield Farm, Dundee, worked with government officials and on his own to find a solution to the blight problem. He sourced varieties from different parts of the world, and with an extensive breeding programme produced an impressive portfolio. One of his varieties, Victoria, became known as the 'Mother of Modern Potatoes' as Archibald Findlay used it to produce Majestic.

10. Potato Marketing Board and dyed potatoes

The Potato Marketing Board was reformed in 1955 to control the area planted via area quotas. It also removed surplus potatoes from the market as stock feed, and these potatoes were dyed green or purple to prevent them returning to shops, with pig and cattle producers taking advantage of the scheme to feed their stock. Spare bottles of dye found many alternative uses such as ammunition for 'blackening' parties.

SCOTTISH DAIRY FARMS

The past century has seen a transformation in the Scottish dairy industry. There were thousands of small farms hand-milking cows and sending the milk off by horse cart and rail to towns and cities. Now, it is much more concentrated, with enterprises consisting of hundreds of cows, all of which are milked in parlours and a growing number in computerised robotic installations where the cow decides when to be milked. Most of the milk now goes to a small number of processors, although a small number of farmers do specialist processing on farm to produce cheese, butter and other products.

Year	1903	1953	1969	1997	2017
No of herds	5,735	8,150	7,338	2,121	957
No of cows	223,666	374,900	329,600	210,000	173,306
Av herd size	39	46	52	99	181
Recorded cows*	1,342	119,698	77,480	130,185	114,963

*Scotland started milk recording early last century, some ten years before England. Official milk recording is now around the 70% mark and growing rapidly. Of the farms not officially recorded, most do make use of the service to test for somatic cell counts, BVD, Johne's disease or pregnancy checking.

YIELDS – AND SEXED SEMEN

Since 1953 average yields have more than doubled, and although herd and cow numbers have decreased, the total output of milk has not altered significantly since then. A large dairy conference in Irvine in 1977 saw several speakers asked to look into the future. Andrew Dunlop of Midkelton said the top herds should reach 1,800 gallons (8,182 litres). This was greeted by remarks such as 'don't be daft' and 'in your dreams'. However, the dreams came true. Current average yields are: Holsteins 8,995 litres; Friesians 6,685 litres; Ayrshires 7,300 litres; and Jerseys 6,035 litres. The same conference saw Jack Lawson, then secretary of the World Federation of Ayrshire Cattle Societies, challenge the agricultural scientists to make Britain first in the field of dictating the sex of a calf before insemination. Sexed semen is now in everyday use.

BREEDS

In 1956, at the Highland Show in Inverness, the Henry Munro News Perpetual Challenge Cup was first presented for the leading interbreed team of dairy cows. The most successful breeds to date are:

Ayrshire – 24
British Friesian – 24
Holstein – 11
Jersey – 2
British Red and White – 2

CHAPTER SEVEN

LUING LIST

Scotland's newest cattle breed emerged from the Island of Luing in 1947 following breeding work by the Cadzow brothers, Shane, Denis and Ralph. However, it took another 18 years for the new beef breed to be officially recognised, in 1965, by the then Secretary of State, Willie Ross. A year later, the first sale of Luings was held in Oban, with the top price of 1,000 guineas being paid for Luing Legend by F.K. Balfour, Dirnanean. The bulls at the sale averaged £735, while the 55 females topped at 180 guineas and averaged £134 thirteen shillings (65pence). Also that year, which was Denis Cadzow's sixtieth birthday, the breed was officially recognised by Parliament. In a publicity drive on 10 August 1968, every hotel in Oban served Luing beef and a caravan on the North Pier served 2,500 Luing steaks in rolls. For their pioneering work in the development of the breed, the Massey Ferguson Award in 1972 went to the Cadzows. This was the first time this prestigious award had come to Scotland. The Cadzows thought showing cattle was a 'fad' and, as a result, Luings are not shown, although they were twice exhibited at the Highland Show some 30 years ago.

TOP LUING PRICES – BULLS

1. 20,000gns – Harehead Mourie in February 2012, from Prof. W.A. Penny, Harehead, Cranshaws, Duns. Sold to P. and S. Crerar, Lammermuir herd, Newmains, Stenton, Dunbar.

2. 17,000gns – Harehead Savivatu in February 2016 from Prof. W.A. Penny, Harehead, Cranshaws, Duns, to P. Simmers, Backmuir, Keith and D. Sawrij, Kedzlie Farms, Lauderdale.

3. 17,000gns – Finlarg Tornado in February 2017 from R. and H. McNee, Over Finlarg, Tealing, Dundee, sold to C.C. MacArthur and Co, Nunnerie, Elvanfoot, Biggar.

4. 14,000gns – Dirnanean Geldof in February 2007 from Finlay McGowan, Incheoch Farms, Alyth, Blairgowrie, bought by Robert McNee, Woodend Farm, Armadale, West Lothian.

5. 14,000gns – Nunnerie Harvey in February 2008, from C.C. MacArthur and Co, Nunnerie, Biggar, bought by Prof. W.A. Penny, Harehead, Cranshaws, Duns.

6. 14,000gns – Milkieston Master in February 2012 from D. and A. Barr, Milkieston, Eddleston, Peebles and sold to C.J. & J.M. Symons, Attonburn, Yetholm, Kelso.

7. 13,000gns – Benhar Kansas in February 2010 from Robert McNee, Woodend Farm, Armadale, West Lothian to E.J. & A.M. Fox, College Luings, Wooler.

8. 12,000gns – Dirnanean Glencoe in February 2007 from Finlay McGowan, Incheoch Farms, Alyth, Blairgowrie, sold to Glen Lyon Estate, Fortingall, Perthshire.

9. 11,500gns – Dirnanean Riley in February 2015 from Finlay McGowan, Incheoch Farms. Alyth, Blairgowrie, sold to P. Simmers, Backmuir, Keith.

FARMERS ON FILM

1. Luke Skywalker – *Star Wars Episode IV: A New Hope* (1977)
It's easy to forget over the course of the original Star Wars Trilogy that the Jedi Knight famous for taking down Darth Vader (AKA 'Dad') started out as a humble farmer. A long time ago in a galaxy far, far away, Luke (Mark Hamill) helped his Uncle Owen run a moisture farm on the planet Tatooine. And just in case there was any doubt about the different skillsets possessed by space pirates and farmers, Han Solo (Harrison Ford) reminds Luke while on board the Millennium Falcon that "travelling through hyperspace ain't like dusting crops, boy!"

2. Ray Kinsella – *Field of Dreams* (1989)
What would you do if you started hearing disembodied voices while alone in an Iowa corn field? Seek therapy or build a baseball field? Ray Kinsella (Kevin Costner) opts for the latter in this tear-jerking fantasy that the star once described as "this generation's It's a Wonderful Life". The phrase "If you build it, they will come" has been absorbed into the language, although farmers may wish to look away when Kinsella ploughs through his perfectly good crops on the advice of a long-dead baseball player.

3. Tom Garvey – *The River* (1984)
Long before he became synonymous with the role of William Wallace in Braveheart, Mel Gibson plays a stubborn Tennessee farmer at odds with his bank manager, his wife and – most significantly – nature itself in this powerful drama based on true events. One of the film's most memorable moments sees Gibson kicking open a series of doors as he hunts for fellow farmer and love rival Joe Wade (Scott Glenn). Thankfully, he stops short of yelling "you may take our corn, but you will never take our freedom".

4. Arthur Hoggett – *Babe* (1995)
Nominated for seven Oscars, there's no doubt that the stars of this hugely popular adaptation of Dick King-Smith's 1983 novel The Sheep-Pig are the animals. But we shouldn't overlook the important role of James Cromwell's farmer Arthur Hoggett, who risks his reputation by letting a pig round up his sheep. And surely there are few other farmers who would launch into an energetic dance routine just to cheer up their livestock. That'll do, pig.

5. The Mexican villagers – *The Magnificent Seven* (1960)
The hopeless plight of the Mexican peasants in John Sturges' iconic western leads Yul Brynner, Steve McQueen, Charles Bronson et al to take a stand against Eli Wallach's fearsome bandits. In a heartwarming ending following much gunfire (incredibly accurate or inaccurate depending on who is doing the shooting), Chico (Horst Buccholz) decides to hang up his holster and tend to the crops with the woman he loves. And to answer the perennial question – who was the seventh member of The Magnificent Seven – the answer is Brad Dexter.

6. Detective John Book – *Witness* (1985)
Harrison Ford's no-nonsense detective goes undercover as an Amish farmer in order to protect a young boy who has witnessed a murder. It could be argued that Book went to the James Bond school of travelling incognito as, before long, he's falling in love with the boy's mother and – in one of the film's most memorable scenes – abandoning his Amish pacifism by punching the lights out of a tormenting local.

7. Joseph Cooper – *Interstellar* (2014)
What is it about farmers in movies that makes them want to blast into deep space rather than mend another tractor or clean out another pig sty? To be fair, 'Coop' Cooper (Matthew McConaughey) has little choice in Christopher Nolan's sci-fi epic as Earth is slowly dying and only the pilot-cum-engineer-cum farmer can save the day – and the planet.

8. Graham Hess – *Signs* (2002)
Capitalising on the media obsession with crop circles, M. Knight Shyamalan's Signs sees Mel Gibson's former priest grow concerned when the pesky phenomena start showing up in his fields. This being the movies, the mysterious circles are actually caused by aliens, as opposed to pranksters with planks of wood and way too much time on their hands.

9. William Munny – *Unforgiven* (1992)
Clint Eastwood directs, produces and stars in this multi Oscar-winning but violent Western that introduced the genre to the Tarantino generation. Once a feared outlaw but now a peace-loving ranch owner, Munny (Eastwood) is tempted out of retirement for one last job. This turns out to be bad news for all concerned, particularly for local sheriff Little Bill Daggett (Gene Hackman).

10. Charles Farmer – *The Astronaut Farmer* (2006)
He may not have the most imaginative surname, but Billy Bob Thornton's frustrated astronaut Charles Farmer is a man who wins the hearts of the people as he attempts to build a fully functioning rocket in the barn of his Texas ranch. Realising he can't fill it up at his diesel tanks, he commits a schoolboy error by arousing the suspicion of the authorities when he goes in search of rocket fuel. Far-fetched, but still a blast.

What is it about farmers in movies that makes them want to blast into deep space rather than mend another tractor or clean out the pig sty?

UNDER-APPRECIATED FARM MACHINERY

Everyone notices the difference in tractors now from their quite basic predecessors, but farming progress has also been down to other less glamorous pieces of equipment. Among the almost forgotten are:

1. Front end loader – a big improvement on the four- or five-tined graip for lifting dung from cattle courts onto trailers. Fewer men were required, less backache was caused and the job was done in half the time.

2. Motorised neep hasher – whether petrol engine or electric motor driven, a big advance on the hand ca'd machines. Saved a man's labour as well as being much quicker, although they couldn't see a stone going in as quickly as a hand ca'er could.

3. Cattle crush – the forerunner would just force the unwilling animal between gates restrained by force of manpower. The crush and its now sophisticated variations have reduced the number of accidents to humans, as well as reducing the stress to the cattle involved.

4. Crop sprayer – modern crop sprayers with hydraulically-operated booms are far more efficient than their predecessors, saving expensive chemicals in avoiding overlaps and not missing bits of the field altogether.

5. Rotating mower – its predecessor, the finger bar mower with reciprocating blades, was be-devilled by stones. Whether drum or disc, the rotating mower can cope with hay or silage grass that is tousled and doesn't have to be cut in a certain direction.

6. Dung spreader – perhaps the first advance over the hand operated graip was the Wild Thwaites spreader which was trailed over the small heaps of muck laid out in rows. Moving floor or rotating flail spreaders provided another step forward in efficiency.

7. Precision seeder – able to set down individual root seeds at a specified distance apart. Precision seeders meant easier thinning, making the hoe redundant, but the machines were not popular with seedsmen who only sold a fraction of the seed they previously did.

8. Elevator – now made redundant by forklifts, they were in their time a big advance over handling manually bags, bales and bunches when they were being lifted to the top of stacks or onto lorries.

9. Bale sledge – hardly used now except for hay/straw for horses, small square bales have been superseded by big bales. The pick-up baler used to spew out small bales every few yards. The bale sledge which either gathered them in a loose clutch or stacked them neatly was a big advance in its time.

ROGUES AND RASCALS

Farmers have a reputation of giving their word and then sticking to it. But, as with all perceived truths, there are exceptions where the thrill of getting one over his fellow man results in one or two individuals breaking the informal conventions. Anonymity has been given to the miscreants but they know who they are:

1. Which farmer, who had half shares in a hay mower with a neighbour, then sold another half share to another neighbour? This resulted in him having use of the machine without having to pay anything for it.

2. Which farmer arranged to have one of his cottages re-slated and then decided not to pay the bill until, on a very wet day, he found the slater removing the slates?

3. Which farmer, whenever faced with one of his old ewes dying, would drag it onto the railway line so he could claim the loss of a high-priced sheep from the railway company?

4. Which farmer arranged to have some rooms measured for fitted carpets, took the measurements from the man surveying the rooms and ordered the carpets elsewhere? So pleased was he that, at a later date, he repeated the ploy. The same surveyor came and took the measurements then meekly handed them over. The delighted farmer again ordered the carpets elsewhere, and when the time came to fit them he couldn't understand why all the carpets were a foot too short.

5. Which farmer, when taking six friends out for a meal, grabbed the bill and then asked them each to pay £xx? It was only later they found he had divided the total excluding himself, thus enjoying a free meal at their expense.

6. Which farmer, when buying cattle from a neighbour on weight, was found unloading dung from his cattle trailer after it had been for an initial 'empty' weigh over the weighbridge before uplifting the stock?

7. Although he was not around to confirm this, as he was in his coffin, one of the above would have been amazed at the large turnout for his funeral. "We are just here to make sure," was the explanation.

FRIEND, FOE – OR IN BETWEEN?

Farming has a mixed relationship with local wildlife – exemplified by listening to bird song while ensuring pigeons do not decimate crops.

WILDLIFE WITH NO REDEEMING FEATURES

1. Pigeons – cause widespread damage on overwintering oilseed rape crops, and many spring sown crops such as peas, brassicas and turnips.

2. Rats and mice – not welcome in and around farm buildings because of their tendency to eat and foul animal and human food.

3. Badgers – their ability to harbour and spread bovine tuberculosis and their diet of helpful creatures like hedgehogs and earthworms make them some cattle farmers' enemy number one.

4. Moles – would be perfectly acceptable if they stayed underground but their habit of leaving mounds of earth make them unpopular with silage makers.

WILDLIFE WITH SOME REDEEMING FEATURES

1. Crows – eat large numbers of harmful grubs like leatherjackets and wireworm, but are not popular when flattening ripening winter barley crops. Some species such as ravens are even less welcome when they peck the eyes and tongues of new-born lambs.

2. Foxes – eat rabbits, but are less popular when they take new-born lambs.

3. Bullfinches – love fruit buds, but can be forgiven because they are beautiful creatures and not normally over-plentiful.

4. Brown hare – used to be a problem on newly singled sugar beet, but since the departure of sugar beet and the large drop in numbers they are now looked on rather more benignly.

5. Over-wintering geese – it has been said that their grazing of anything green helps crops tiller; this cannot be said on heavy soils where their paddling kills off braids or where grazing is scarce in some less favoured areas.

IT SEEMED A GOOD IDEA AT THE TIME...

1. Rabbits – the Romans first brought them to Britain but they were not established in the wild until the 12th Century. They had a knock back with myxomatosis in the 1950s, but are now as big a pest as ever.

2. Grey squirrel – introduced from America in 1876 and released by landowners in England. They have been blamed for the demise of the native red squirrel.

3. American mink – first imported to fur farms in Britain from Canada and Alaska in 1929. Animal fur is no longer politically correct, but the mink in the wild have been a problem, almost eliminating the water vole population.

4. Sea eagles – re-introduced from Norway and while they delight environmentalists they are not popular with sheep farmers who lose lambs to this predator.

5. Beavers – another species which has been re-introduced and they add to the biodiversity of the countryside. They are not, however, welcome in arable areas where their disruption of the drainage systems does not fit with high input farming.

TRADITIONAL SONGS WITH A RURAL THEME

1. *My Blue Grey Coos* – by Charlie Allan, extolling the virtues of this once-popular cross between a Whitebred Shorthorn bull and a Galloway cow over other farm animals.

2. *Wha saw the Tattie Howkers* – a parody on Wha saw the 42nd. A Glasgow bairns' song reputedly describing the departing Irish potato pickers going down the Clyde.

3. *Muckin o' Geordie's Byre* – bothy ballad in the Doric describing this necessary part of livestock husbandry.

4. *Soor Milk Cairt* – 'Drivin intae Glesga in ma soor milk cairt'. Describes the journey from Eaglesham to Glasgow and the comments from the young woman he was giving a lift to.

5. *Aikey Brae* – another bothy ballad describing a visit to the Aikey Horse Fair in Buchan where heavy horses were bought and sold.

6. *McGinty's meal and ale* – …phar the pig gaed on the spree. This was the name of a food and drink business where the antics of a pig on the loose are well described.

7. *Nicky Tams* – another from the North East describing the pros and cons of wearing leather straps just below the knees on working breeks.

8. *Berry Fields o' Blair* – the late Belle Stewart, well known traveller and song writer, wrote this song in 1947 at the request of her family for their Hogmany party. It describes the variety of people from across Scotland who came for the annual Blairgowrie berry-picking.

9. *Barnyards o' Delgaty* – one more bothy ballad about a feeing market and the subsequent work on the named farm. This was quite a prestigious farm and the ballad is poking a bit of fun at it.

10. *Rolling hills of the Border* – extolling the landscape of the border country as opposed to other beauty spots nationally and internationally. Made for funerals; 'when I die bury me low…'

'McGinty's meal and ale - ⋯⋯⋯⋯
phar the pig gaed on the spree'.

AGRICULTURAL BOOKS OF THE EIGHTEENTH AND NINETEENTH CENTURIES

Scotland had a number of eminent agricultural writers. Some of them were best-selling authors, known well-beyond the boundaries of Scotland, influencing and shaping agricultural practice wherever they were read.

1. James Small, *A treatise on ploughs and wheel carriages*, 1774
Small was a key figure in the Scottish 'agricultural revolution', introducing a lightweight plough from Rotherham to replace the heavy Scots plough which had to be pulled by four oxen. His book was the first book on ploughs and ploughing in Scotland.

2. Henry Home, Lord Kames, *The gentleman farmer*, 1776
Kames was an eminent agriculturist, landowner, agricultural 'improver', and central figure of the Scottish enlightenment. His best-selling treatise extended to six editions until 1815. It is a practical guide, also including descriptions of the implements used on farms.

3. Board of Agriculture, *County agricultural surveys*, 1793-1817
Sir John Sinclair of the Statistical Account of Scotland fame was the brainchild behind this extensive survey of Britain. It provided for the first time a systematic account of the agriculture and rural economy of each county throughout Britain.

4. William Aiton, A *treatise on the dairy breed of cows and dairy husbandry, with an account of the Lanarkshire breed of horses*, 1825
Aiton was a highly regarded agricultural writer, and became one of the most prolific agricultural journalists of the day from the mid-1840s. His book is a detailed account of two key livestock species in the 'agricultural revolution'.

5. J.C. Loudon, *An encyclopedia of agriculture*, 1825
Loudon was a botanist, garden designer, author and garden magazine editor. His encyclopedia is an extensive account of agriculture on systematic principles.

6. David Low, *Elements of practical agriculture*, 1839
This is the best-known treatise of the Professor of Agriculture at Edinburgh University. Low recognised that a county's agriculture was affected in its general details and practice by climate, the soil's fertility, and the food and habits of the people.

7. James Smith, *Remarks on thorough draining and deep ploughing*, 1831
Smith was at the centre of the drainage 'revolution', which brought underground tile drainage to fields and the modern look of fields that we have today. His book, which ran to several editions, was highly influential.

8. Henry Stephens, *The book of the farm*, 1844

This book was extended to a number of editions and continued to be published after his death. This was the best-known agricultural book of the nineteenth century. It was translated into several languages, and widely sold across Europe. It is a store of information on agricultural practices, implements and machines.

9. Highland and Agricultural Society of Scotland, *Report on the present state of the agriculture of Scotland*, 1878

A contemporary survey of Scottish agriculture before the agricultural depression that extended into the first decade of the twentieth century and changed the face of Scottish agriculture.

10. Alexander Ramsay, *History of the Highland and Agricultural Society of Scotland*, 1879

Ramsay was Secretary of the Highland and Agricultural Society of Scotland and an eminent agricultural writer. His book provides a detailed history of the society and its activities, including the Highland Show, and its influence.

BRED AT THE JAMES HUTTON INSTITUTE

Over the past 90 years, the James Hutton Institute and its many predecessors, including the Scottish Crop Research Institute and the Scottish Horticultural Institute, has produced many new varieties in a wide range of crops. These include:

1. Brassicas – several varieties of kale and other fodder crops were bred, and an impressive list of swede varieties with Scottish names including Brora and Gowrie.

2. Cereals – spring barley varieties Tweed and Tyne and a dozen oat varieties from Albyn Bard to Shearer. The James Hutton Institute is now at the centre of the Barley Hub project aimed at breeding new varieties through unravelling its DNA.

3. Lilies – started as a sideline by Dr Christopher North in the 1960s and 70s, the objective was to produce shorter, disease-resistant hybrids, more suited to Scottish conditions. His work was carried on by another enthusiast, Dr Peter Waister.

4. Grasses – Scotia Cocksfoot, Scotia Timothy and Scotia Perennial Ryegrass were bred in earlier years, but in the 1970s grass and oat breeding was transferred to the Welsh Plant Breeding Station.

5. Potatoes – from the earlier prefixed Roslin and Craigs varieties to the more recent Pentland range, the stations have produced dozens of new cultivars. Pentland Dell is still widely used and more recent successes include Mayan Gold, Vales Sovereign and Lady Balfour.

6. Blackcurrants – with the 'Ben' prefix, a score of varieties such as Ben Lomond and Ben Nevis have been produced. It has been reckoned that 50% of global blackcurrant production comes from varieties bred in Scotland.

7. Raspberries – the 'Glen' family has covered many acres of raspberry plantations, from the once widely-grown Glen Clova to the more recent Glen Ample. Raspberry work began at Dundee as an offshoot of East Malling in Kent, charged with investigating rasp virus diseases.

8. Strawberries – Red Gauntlet and Auchincruive Climax go back a bit, but more recently the institute produced Symphony, with a tougher skin than Elsanta in order to stand up to Scottish conditions.

9. Other soft fruit – Mylnefield has produced three varieties of brambles or as it describes them, blackberries. It has also bred the blackberry/raspberry hybrid known as the tayberry, which has a niche market in farm shops and gardens.

THE 10 COUNTIES GROWING THE MOST OATS IN 1917

One hundred years ago, oats were essential in feeding both horses and people. The acreage of the crop was considerable as can be seen from the figures below unearthed from Government archives.

1. Aberdeen 896,317 quarters produced from 193,825 acres, at 37 bushels per acre. Only 2% of that area was still being grown as oats in Aberdeen 'county' in 2016. One quarter is 8 bushels or 0.3 cubic metres.

2. Perth 473,910 quarters from 76,293 acres, at 50 bushels per acre. About 5% of that area was growing oats in Perth 'county' in 2016.

3. Forfar (aka Angus) 395,470 quarters from 59,027 acres at 54 bushels per acre, the highest yield in Scotland at the time. Just over 4% of that area was growing oats in 2016. In 2016, the average yield in Scotland was the equivalent of 169 bushels per acre. That's progress.

4. Ayr 290,101 quarters from 47,974 acres, at 48 bushels per acre. Hardly any oats grown in Ayr 'county' in 2016.

5. Fife 282,596 quarters from 47,191 acres, at 48 bushels per acre. About 10% of that area was growing oats in 2016, making Fife the county in the top ten which has maintained the highest proportion of its 1917 oats area, though Clackmannanshire (not in the top 10) had 12 per cent of its 1917 figure in 2016.

6. Banff 270,177 quarters from 49,371 acres, at 44 bushels per acre. About 3% of that area was growing oats in what would be Banff in 2016.

7. Lanark 242,006 quarters from 43,968 acres, at 44 bushels per acre. About 1% of that area was growing oats in 2016.

8. Dumfries 223,339 quarters from 44,622 acres, at 40 bushels per acre. About 1% of that area was growing oats in 2016.

9. Wigtown 190,388 quarters from 33,158 acres, at 46 bushels per acre. About 1% of that area was growing oats in 2016.

10. Ross and Cromarty 176,792 quarters from 34,238 acres, at 41 bushels per acre. About 2% of that area was growing oats in 2016.

WHAT WERE?

1. Rabbit clearance societies – in 1958 the government introduced the rabbit clearance society scheme, awarding a grant of 50% to societies towards co-ordinated rabbit control costs. During the mid 1950s, an estimated 99% of the rabbit population had been killed by myxomatosis and the scheme was seen as a means of trying to maintain at a low level or even further reduce rabbit numbers.

2. The Green Pound – to protect farmers from the daily fluctuations of the currencies of the various European countries, European politicians agreed a fixed exchange or green rate. Unfortunately for farmers in the UK, almost throughout its existence from 1973 until the arrival of the euro in 1999, this green rate or 'green pound' disadvantaged them badly.

3. Flax – the treaty of Union in 1707 and the financial adjustments at the time included an inducement for more flax growing in Scotland. Although the crop lost out to cereals in the mid 19th century, brief revivals occurred during both World Wars.

4. Deficiency payments – the 1947 Agriculture Act introduced a range of guaranteed prices for cereals and livestock. Deficiency payments were paid to each farmer when the market price fell below the guaranteed price. They were discontinued when the UK joined the Common Market.

5. Potato holidays – the mid-autumn break in the school year is still called the tattie holidays in the East of Scotland. In 1949, 44,000 schoolchildren were employed picking potatoes. It was back-breaking but character forming work and the kids loved their pay, but mechanisation stopped it in the 1980s.

6. Price review – the arrival of guaranteed prices for farm produce post-war required a mechanism for setting these prices. This was the annual price review, a series of meetings between the government minister, his civil servants and the representatives of the farmers' unions of England, Scotland, Wales and Northern Ireland.

7. Scottish sugar beet industry – a processing factory was built near Cupar in 1924 and continued until it was closed in 1971. Sugar beet was a valuable crop in the rotation in Fife, Perth and Angus but yields could never compete with those in the south. Now even in England, sugar beet is only grown in the most favoured areas.

8. Marketing boards – established in the 1930s to stabilise prices and regulate production for milk, potatoes and eggs. They were revived post-war and survived political threat in the Thatcher years but eventually fell to incompatibility with EU regulations. The Wool Marketing Board, however, continues to this day.

9. Agricultural Executive Committees – established at the outset of World War II to optimise farm production. They had extraordinary powers to persuade farmers to turn more grazing land over to crops, and to ensure farming practice was up to scratch.

CHAPTER EIGHT

TOP FARMING BUSINESSES

Scotland has a large number of farming-related businesses. Among the many listed with Companies House are (in alphabetical order):

1. Angus Soft Fruits – this Arbroath-based company is one of the biggest soft fruit producers in Scotland. Set up in 1994 by the Porter and Gray families, the company is a producer organisation with 18 members located primarily in Angus, Fife and Perthshire. For the year ended April 30, 2016, it recorded a turnover of £95.09m and pre-tax profits of £531,997. It employs 128 members of staff.

2. ANM Group – the north-east farmers' co-operative runs Europe's largest livestock auction facility at the Thainstone Centre in Inverurie. For the year ended December 31, 2016, the co-op posted pre-tax profits of £189,000. Turnover, which represents commission earned by the group, was £8.62million while throughput was £124.78m. It sold 83,500 cattle and 311,000 sheep in the year.

3. Bartlett International Holdings – also known as Albert Bartlett, this Airdrie-based company is one of Scotland's largest tattie processors. For the year ended May 31, 2016, it posted a turnover of £149.03m and pre-tax profits of £5.51m. It employs more than 800 people.

4. Davidsons Animal Feeds – this animal feed firm based at Shotts in North Lanarkshire employs more than 60 people. For the year ended July 31, 2016, the company recorded turnover of £25.94m and pre-tax profits of £403,456.

5. Farmlay Eggs – the north-east egg company, which supplies Morrisons, Aldi and Lidl in Scotland, packs about four million eggs a week. Run by the Chapman family, all eggs are sourced from the family farm and a network of 23 contract producers. For the year ended May 31, 2016, the company recorded a turnover of £15.35million and pre-tax profits of £2.38million. It employs 40 people.

6. First Milk – this Glasgow-headquartered company is 100% owned by UK dairy farmers. In the year ended March 31, 2016, the co-op posted turnover of £291.45m and a pre-tax loss of £3.44m.

7. J.W. Galloway – this family-owned business is Scotland's largest red meat processor. It owns Scotbeef, Vivers Scotland and a majority share in Scotbeef (Inverurie). For the year ended February 28, 2016, it recorded a turnover of £311.07m and pre-tax profits of £4.43m. It employs more than 960 people.

8. Galloway and Macleod – this grain miller and agricultural merchant is based in Stonehouse, Lanarkshire. For the year ended August 31, 2016, it posted turnover of £11.05m and pre-tax profits of £15,372.

9. Glenrath Farms – this Peebles-based company is Scotland's largest egg producer. Founded by Sir John Campbell and now run by his family, the company produces a range of different eggs including Kitty Campbell's Free Range Eggs and Big and Scottish. For the year ended May 31, 2016, it recorded a turnover of £51.71m and pre-tax profits of £8.19m.

10. Graham's The Family Dairy – this family-owned business is Scotland's largest privately-owned dairy company. Based at Bridge of Allan, it also has milk processing sites in Nairn and Fife. For the year ended March 31, 2016, it posted turnover of £83.6m and pre-tax profits of £1.43m.

11. Harbro Group – the Turriff-headquartered animal feed manufacturer employs more than 400 people and runs a network of 19 retail stores. For the year ended June 30, 2016, it posted a turnover of £100.36m and pre-tax profits of £3.48m.

12. Kettle Produce – this Fife-based company is Scotland's main vegetable and salad crop processor. For the year ended May 31, 2016, it recorded a turnover of £113.56m and pre-tax profits of £2.37m. During the year the firm employed a monthly average of 1,021 people.

13. Norvite Animal Nutrition – this animal feed firm is based near Oldmeldrum in Aberdeenshire and employs more than 70 people. For the year ended May 31, 2016 it recorded turnover of £12.5m and pre-tax profits of £203,164.

14. Ringlink – the organisation is Scotland's largest machinery ring. For the year ended July 31, 2016, it recorded a turnover of £1.16m and pre-tax profits of £4,881. Its labour and training division – Ringlink Services – posted turnover of £4.86m and pre-tax profits of £120,394 in the same period.

MOST WIDELY GROWN WARE AND SEED POTATO VARIETIES IN SCOTLAND 1936

1. Kerr's Pink (32,744 acres) Raised by J.F. Henry, Banff in 1907 and marketed by Kerr in 1917. Late maincrop, creamy white flesh with much sought-after high dry matter described as floury, in Scotland. Also used for chipping, crisping and baking.

2. Majestic (14,878 acres) Bred by Archibald Findlay, Auchtermuchty and first marketed in 1917. Early maincrop. Very popular in England. It became a market leader for the next 60 years. Most modern varieties can be traced back to this through their pedigrees.

3. King Edward (13,974 acres) First named and marketed by J. Butler in 1902. Early maincrop, susceptible to wart disease and very susceptible to blight. Part coloured pink, confined to the eyes and rose ends. Slightly mealy potatoes with cream white flesh.

4. Epicure (9,200 acres) Raised by J. Clark, Christchurch, and marketed by Messrs Sutton and Sons in 1897. First early, probably the earliest British variety of commercial importance. The plants recover rapidly from frost damage to the foliage. Firm texture with distinctive flavour.

5. Great Scot (7,447 acres) Bred by E. Miles, Mickleholm, and marketed in 1909. Early maincrop. Immune to wart disease and very resistant to dry rot. It is suited to a range of climates and is popular in India. Disintegration is negligible but slight, but after cooking blackening may occur.

6. Golden Wonder (7,017 acres) Introduced by J. Brown, Arbroath, in 1904. A russet variant of the variety Maincrop raised by J. Clark, Christchuch in 1876 out of a berry from Early Rose and renamed Langworthy by J. Niven, Perth in 1905. Late maincrop. Susceptible to primary leafroll which causes net necrosis (not spraing) of the tuber. Dry and mealy, on boiling disintegration is sometimes severe.

7. Doon Star (2,714 acres) Bred by Messrs McGill and Smith, Ayr 1928. An early maincrop. High yields, but prone to internal rust spot. Although suitable for crisp production, commercial use of the variety has been restricted, probably because of the problems of satisfactory storage. Oval tubers with white creamy flesh, slight mealiness.

8. Arran Banner (2,608 acres) Bred by D. Mackelvie, Arran in 1927. Early maincrop grown in Scotland and Northern Ireland, mainly for export in particular to Cyprus and Malta. Considerable tolerance to drought. Dry matter content is medium to low.

9. British Queen (2,262 acres) Bred by Archibald Findlay, then Markinch, in 1894 from Paterson's 'Victoria'. The variety had more than 94 synonyms: Dalmeny Radium, Maid of Auchterarder and Shan't be Long, to name a few. Still marketed on the roadside in Ireland as the second early known simply as 'Queens'. Best enjoyed boiled in their skins with stew.

TOP ADVANTAGES OF LIVING IN THE COUNTRYSIDE FOR PRIMARY SCHOOL CHILDREN

1. Feeding pet lambs – a useful job for farm children, taking some of the work load off their parents and introducing them to basic animal husbandry.

2. Lambing a ewe – more advanced animal husbandry but gives an opportunity to explain how it got in there in the first place without having to resort to the birds and the bees. It also proves that lambs are not all white and woolly when they first arrive.

3. Jumping in puddles – sure they have puddles in towns, but not as big or as muddy as those round the farmyard and the mud stains as they dried on your clothes are a badge of honour.

4. Spending the day in your wellies – apart from the fact that there are no laces to tie, so easy to slip on and off, they provide flexible footwear for any occasion, and kids don't care about trench foot and sweaty, smelly feet.

5. Riding your bike free from traffic – farm roads and farmyards are a safe place for any amount of high jinks on bikes, scooters or carts and a concrete surface would surely do for skateboards or roller skates as well.

6. Playing on straw – since straw and hay handling has advanced, the opportunity for jumping off a straw soo stack onto a heap of loose straw has diminished. Playing on a stack of small bales is still fun but playing on big bales is best avoided.

7. Riding on a tractor – with an adult at the controls it is still possible to imagine you are driving if you can get your hands on the steering wheel, and far more cool than driving a car.

8. Snowed in and missing school – much more likely than for kids living in towns where snow clearance is more urgent, but this can be negated if the friendly farmer offers to take the children to school in the big four wheel drive tractor.

9. Building huts and dens – tools from the farm workshop are readily available for constructing these secret places, far away from prying adult eyes where your imagination is the only limit to who or where you can be.

10. Learning where your food comes from – and not being aware you are learning at all. You know from an early age that milk comes from cows, eggs from hens, potatoes from the soil and they don't originate in the supermarket.

11. Freedom to roam – up the hill or in the woods. Parents know that the countryside is a relatively safe environment and healthier for mind and body than playing indoors on electronic gadgetry.

He planned on missing school . . .

SCOTTISH WOMEN'S INSTITUTES

Formerly the SWRI or just 'The Rural', and currently celebrating its 100th year in existence, it was set up by East Lothian farmer's wife Catherine Blair. She was active in the suffragette movement, and recognised a need for women living in rural areas to gain the benefits of education and training in home skills, family welfare and citizenship.

Her vision was shared by others, and 37 women turned up to a meeting at Longniddry in June 1917, where the first institute was formed and is still in existence today.

The network spread across the country, and the SWI now stretches from Shetland to the Borders, and the Western Isles to the East Neuk of Fife.

A total of 16,000 members attend more than 700 Institutes in 32 Federation areas. Now, as well as cake decorating, embroidery techniques and floral art, meetings are just as likely to feature gin tasting, life drawing, upcycling and ukulele playing.

New-style meetings reflecting a wider range of interests and held at flexible times and in venues such as pubs and coffee shops have been introduced in the past two years, while the word 'rural' was dropped from the organisation's title to become inclusive of women living in towns and cities as well as country areas. These changes have resulted in new branches being formed in urban areas.

Even the traditional scone has taken a modern twist, as this list of 10 of the most unusual flavours from SWI members highlights:

10 MOST UNUSUAL SCONE FLAVOURS

1. Marmite and cheese

2. Mars bar

3. Courgette and herb

4. Cumin seed and tomato

5. Carrot and banana

6. Brie and cranberry

7. Haggis and cheese

8. Apple and walnut

9. Orange and ginger

10. Cherry and almond

ARTICLES PUBLISHED BY THE DEPARTMENT OF AGRICULTURE FOR SCOTLAND IN THE 1950S AND 1960S

1. Water and Electricity Supplies on Farms in Scotland
Published in 1950, written by J. Wrigley, it gives detailed results from a 1948 questionnaire showing that 21% of farms had public mains water and 23% had electricity.

2. Sales of Farm Land during 1950
Published in 1951, written by P.M. Scola, an analysis of Inland Revenue data suggested that half of sales involved changing land from tenanted to owner-occupied.

3. Agricultural Output in Scotland by Regions
Published in 1954, written by H.J. Shemilt, it gives 1951/52 data on output in five regions of Scotland. The figures suggest a slightly higher share of output in both the Highlands and North East than we see nowadays, and slightly lower share in the East, with the South West and South East unchanged.

4. Changes in the Geographical Distribution of Cows
Published in 1956, written by P.M. Scola and including three maps, the article describes areas of particular growth during a time when cattle numbers were generally increasing.

5. The Small Farm in Scotland
Published in 1957, written by G.F. Hendry and O.J. Beilby, its six sections covered 'Its place in Scottish agriculture', 'The financial position', 'Use of resources compared with larger farms', 'Economic success factors', 'Non-economic success factors', and 'Conclusions'.

6. The Size of Scotland's Bracken Problem
Published in 1958, written by G.F. Hendry, it shows the extent of bracken infestation, including a detailed map. There was an estimated 450,000 acres of bracken, a quarter of which was in Argyll. The area had increased by 10,000 acres since 1943.

7. Scotland's Farm Population
Published in 1961, written by O.J. Beilby, it gives the results of a sample survey for the United Nations' FAO World Census. It suggested that 6% of Scotland's population lived on a farm, with farms having an average of six persons resident on them.

8. The Displacement of Oats by Barley in Scotland
Published in 1964, written by L.V. McEwan, it listed reasons for the change as mechanisation of farming and the resultant drop in demand for horse-feed, new varieties of barley, introduction of the combine harvester, demands of the brewing industry, trends in silage making and the introduction of slatted floor cattle housing.

SUFFOLK SHEEP

With their distinctive black faces, Suffolks first emerged more than 200 years ago after Norfolk Horn ewes were mated to Southdown rams in the Bury St Edmunds area. The first Scottish flock of Suffolks was established in Scotland in 1895 and from that date the breed has gone on to be one of the top terminal sires in the sheep industry. The breed is noted for its quick fleshing ability and the ewes for their easy lambing.

TOP TEN AUCTION PRICES FOR SUFFOLK RAMS (AT 1/6/17)
All prices in guineas which equal £1.05

1. 90,000gns Ardlea Arbinnig from Dan Tynan, Ardlea, Co. Laois to Myfyr Evans, Rhaeadr at Stirling in 2011.

2. 75,000gns Stockton Almighty from W.H. Sinnet, Stockton, Worcs to T. & J. Bailey, Co. Meath at Edinburgh in 1998.

3. 70,000gns Rhaeadr Rossi from Myfyr Evans, Rhaeadr to T. & J. Bailey, Baileys, Co. Meath at Edinburgh in 2006.

4. 68,000gns Muiresk King of Diamonds from S. G. Mair & Sons, Kinnermit, Turriff to J. Douglas, Cairness, Fraserburgh at Edinburgh in 1995.

5. 62,000gns Cairness Castello from J. Douglas, Cairness, Fraserburgh to I. & J. Barbour, at Edinburgh in 2009.

6. 60,000gns Muiresk Momento from S.G. Mair & Sons, Kinnermit, Turriff to J. Douglas, Cairness, Fraserburgh at Edinburgh in 2003.

7. 54,000gns Stockton Storm from W. H. Sinnett & Sons, Stockton, Worcs to J. Douglas, Cairness, Fraserburgh and S. G. Mair & Sons, Kinnermit, Turriff, at Edinburgh in 1997.

8. 50,000gns Stockton Caesars Son from W. H. Sinnett, Stockton, Worcs to J. Douglas, Cairness, Fraserburgh and S.G. Mair & Sons, Kinnermit, Turriff, at Edinburgh in 1999.

9. 48,000gns Stockton Mega Ram from W.H. Sinnett, Stockton, Worcs to T. & J. Bailey, Baileys, Co. Meath at Edinburgh in 1997.

10. 48,000gns Strathisla Dylan Thomas from R. Wilson, North Dorlaithers, Turriff to H. Stewart at Edinburgh in 2007.

A TOWNIE VIEW OF THE COUNTRYSIDE

1. Barbed wire hurts, especially if you're trying to climb over it.

2. What looks like sun-hardened cow poo isn't necessarily.

3. Picking raspberries and strawberries is fun only for a short spell.

4. Private road means that down that road there's likely to be a person who will shout at you.

5. Dogs on farms haven't necessarily learned how to welcome strangers politely.

6. Baths in fields are not for ablutions.

7. What looks like a neglected field of scrub and thistles can actually be earning a farmer some money.

8. Hay bales are harder to climb and more uncomfortable to sit on than you would think.

9. China eggs are not edible.

10. Gates into fields require a lot of negotiation. Padlocks would be easier to understand than the loops of rope and wire twisted into something that only a Scout would recognise.

Baths in fields are not for ablutions.

THE FIRST TOWNS IN SCOTLAND WITH CATTLE AUCTION MARTS

For more than 160 years, livestock auction marts have provided financially secure buyers for the farmers of Scotland. By 1860, ten towns in Scotland had been provided with purpose-built permanent pens in 12 markets, the first of which was at Hawick and the sole survivor still selling is at Lockerbie. In 1939, more than 220 marts were in operation, but by 2017 only 24 remain. The first 12 established were:

1. Hawick in 1817 – Andrew Oliver

2. Perth in 1830 – Alexander Hay

3. Perth in 1858 – Macdonald and MacCallum

4. Haddington in 1858 – Francis Vert

5. Kelso in 1859 – Fairbairn and Penny

6. Dundee in 1859 – Alec Rae

7. Dalkeith in 1859 – Thomas Dodds

8. Edinburgh in 1860 – R. Buist

9. Glasgow in 1860 – Thomas Spence

10. Lockerbie in 1860 – James Rossell

11. Wick in 1860 – Alexander Sinclair

12. Edinburgh in 1860 – John Swan

Information supplied by John Thomson, author of *Ring of Memories*.

BRITISH SIMMENTALS

The first importation of Simmentals from Switzerland and Germany arrived in Dundee on August 7, 1970 and one month later 259 heifers and 12 bulls were released from quarantine. On August 25, 1970, the inaugural meeting of the British Simmental Society was held and the breed made its first public appearance at the Royal Highland Show, Ingliston in 1971. In October 1972, auctioneer Jack Young sold the first Simmental bull in Perth. Overhall Allendorf from Tom Neilson, Overhall, Harlow, Essex made 2,400 guineas to Ken Durston, East Nevay, Forfar, Angus.

TOP UK SIMMENTAL BULL PRICES AT AUCTION

1. 45,000gns – Bel Dhu Capercaillile from Anne Macpherson, Blackford Simmentals, Inverness to W.J. and J. Green, Corskie Simmentals, Fochabers and Smallburn Farms, Elgin. (February 2013)

2. 25,000gns – Corskie Gingersnap from W.J. and J. Green, Corskie Simmentals, Fochabers, Moray to J.H. and V.G. Wood, Popes Simmentals, Preston, Lancashire. (October 2016)

3. 22,000gns – Omorga Samson from H.J.W. and J.C. Moore, Omorga Simmentals, Co. Tyrone to Strathisla Farms, Strathisla Simmentals, Meigle, Perthshire. (February 2007)

4. 22,000gns – Dirnanean Typhoon from Finlay McGowan, Dirnanean Simmentals, Blairgowrie, Perthshire to Mr and Mrs D. Field, Burytown Simmentals, Wiltshire. (February 2008)

5. 22,000gns – Dirnanean Bradley from Finlay McGowan, Dirnanean Simmentals, Blairgowrie, Perthshire to W.J. and J. Green, Corskie Simmentals, Fochabers, Moray. (October 2011)

6. 22,000gns – Kilbride Farm Foreman from W.H. Robson & Sons, Kilbride Farm Simmentals, Ballyclare, Co. Antrim to Clive Houldey, Manor Park Simmentals, Lockerbie, Dumfriesshire. (February 2016)

7. 21,000gns – Corrick Kentucky Kid from Cecil McIlwaine. Corrick Simmentals, Newton Stewart, Co. Tyrone to A.R. Clements, Darsham Simmentals, Suffolk. (February 2001)

8. 21,000gns – Overhill House Guinness from Richard McCulloch, Overhill House Simmentals, Armadale, West Lothian to A. Thomson, Glasgow. (February 2017)

9. 20,000gns – Slievenagh Talisman from Robin Boyd, Slievenagh Simmentals, Co. Antrim to R.H. Widdicombe, Starline Simmentals, Devon. (November 2007)

10. 20,000gns – Annick Talisker from Lachlan Quarm, Annick Simmentals, Irvine, Ayrshire to Hector MacAskill, Woodhall Simmentals, Dunbar, East Lothian. (February 2008)

SCOTTISH PLANT COLLECTORS

Scottish plant collectors scoured the globe to bring new species back to their home country. Among the most famous were:

1. Robert Fortune – served an apprenticeship in the gardens of Kelloe, Berwickshire, then with the Horticultural Society in Chiswick. He impressed them as a gardener and botanist and was appointed to go to China to collect plants. He collected tea seedlings there and in 1851 arrived in Calcutta with 2,000 young tea plants and 17,000 germinating seeds – laying the foundation for the Indian tea trade. His British introductions include many flowering shrubs and herbaceous specimens.

2. Archibald Menzies – born in 1754, he went to school in Weem and then worked for a time in the garden at Castle Menzies. He graduated with a medical degree but entered the navy and, being based in America, became familiar with the local flora. He travelled widely in North and South America and among his introductions to this country are the Monkey Puzzle tree, Lawson's Cyprus and Red Cedar.

3. David Douglas – best known as the namesake of the Douglas fir. He was born in Scone and worked as a gardener before exploring North America. He introduced several hundred plants to Britain and hence to Europe, and more than 80 species have douglasii in their scientific names.

4. George Forrest – born in Falkirk and became one of the first explorers of China's remote south west province of Yunnan, generally regarded as the most bio-diverse in the country. He brought back 31,000 plant specimens, discovered numerous species and the specific epithet forrestii now adorns more than 30 genera.

5. George Sherriff – fought in the First World War, after which he joined the diplomatic service where he met naturalist Frank Ludlow. The two made several expeditions to the Himalayas, collecting thousands of species. On returning to Scotland, Sherriff bought the estate of Ascreavie in Angus where he cultivated a collection of Himalayan plants.

6. David Lyall – after studying medicine in Aberdeen he was appointed for service in the Royal Navy and, as assistant surgeon, had to make botanical collections. His worldwide travels enabled him to make extensive herbarium collections. His many flowering and structural plants introductions include Hebe, and he has the rare distinction of a genus Lyallia named after him.

7. Euan Cox – accompanied Reginald Farrer on his last botanical expedition to Burma in 1919. Many of the plants collected and introduced to Britain were rhododendron and other flowering shrubs. Cox was a very successful propagator of rhododendrons and had an extensive collection at Glendoick, Perthshire, later run by his son Peter and grandson Kenneth.

CHAPTER NINE

ENDANGERED WILDLIFE

1. Corn bunting – the 'fat bird of the barley' is an arable farming specialist found primarily in Aberdeenshire and Fife. Farmers have been encouraged by RSPB to use options within governmental schemes which increase seed- and insect-rich habitats and decrease nest destruction. This has led to increases on farms undertaking corn bunting-friendly management.

2. Marsh Fritillary butterfly – in Scotland this butterfly is found in south Lochaber, Argyll and the Argyll islands. Its survival relies on extensive grazing of flower-rich grassland to maintain it in suitable condition. Devil's bit scabious are essential as they are the caterpillar's sole food plant.

3. Corncrake – more likely heard than seen, this iconic species is recorded during summer, mostly on islands in west Scotland including Coll, Tiree, Islay and Uists. Crofters, working with conservation organisations, have helped turn round the fortunes of this species with more than 400 males recorded in Scotland in 2017.

4. Black grouse – found on moorland, rough grazings and newly planted forestry in upland areas of Scotland. The best time to see this species is between March and May when the males get together to display at sites called leks.

5. Great yellow bumblebee – once found throughout the UK, this species is now restricted to the North coast of Scotland and some Scottish islands, making it one of the rarest bumblebees in the UK. Crofters are encouraged to manage the machair sympathetically for this species by maintaining the flower-rich environment.

6. Curlew – with its amazing curved bill, long legs and resonating call, curlew is one of the most charismatic species in the UK. The UK holds between 20% and 25% of the global breeding population with most found on upland areas. Unfortunately, research has shown that numbers over the last few decades have declined. Conservation groups are working with farmers to develop solutions which will reverse these declines.

7. Brown hare – most visible during early spring when adults can be seen boxing, brown hares prefer open areas such as grassland and arable. They are regularly recorded in southern Scotland but absent from the north and most of the islands.

8. Irish lady's-tresses – this small wild orchid has small creamy-white flowers. It grows in marshy grassland in the west of Britain and Ireland and can be managed by careful grazing regimes.

OLDEST FARMING CLUBS/SOCIETIES

1. Teviotdale Farmers Club – formed in 1859 by local auctioneer James Oliver and is still going strong. The Oliver family were secretaries of the club from the beginning right up to 1994.

2. SWI – the first 'Rural' was formed in Longniddry in 1917. It only managed to claim first spot after neighbouring Macmerry had to postpone its meeting because of an outbreak of measles.

3. Tarff Valley Agricultural Cooperative Society – instituted in 1903 by Walter Montgomerie Neilson of Queenshill, Ringford. It is very active to this day, supplying 'all farmers' needs' in southern Scotland and the North of England.

4. The Scottish Women's Agricultural Association – formed 113 years ago by dairymaids from across Scotland. They used to meet in Edinburgh where they held a butter-making competition in the Waverley Market.

5. The Board of Agriculture – set up in the early nineteenth century. But another Board of Agriculture was set up in 1913; this was a Government department and forerunner to 'The Department' we know today.

6. Kilmarnock branch of the NFUS – formed in late 1913 and had as its president the parent body's own first president, William Donald of Fardalehill. Kilmarnock branch continues to this day as part of the Ayrshire region.

7. Scotways – established in 1845 and is the UK's oldest outdoor access group; it says, "We work to protect and develop access to the Scottish countryside for all".

8. Central and West Fife Agricultural Society – started life back in 1760 where the 'Chicken Pie Club' met annually in Crossgates. The Dunfermline Farmers' Society met annually in Dunfermline and these two societies united in 1834 under the name of the Western District of Fife Agricultural Association. This body, under the name of a Society rather than Association, merged with Leslie and Kinglassie Agricultural Society to form the Central and West Fife Agricultural Society who run West Fife Show to this day.

9. Borders Machinery Ring (BMR) – the first ring to be formed in the UK in February 1987 by 23 farmers and contractors, it has the aim of rationalising labour, machinery and input costs. There are now nine rings in Scotland and 15 in England and Wales.

10. Lanergill, Caithness was the first Young Farmers Club in Scotland. It was formed in 1923 by James Robson, Lynegar, following a visit to the United States where he saw the extensive 4H organisation for young people living and working in rural areas.

THE 10 MOST POPULAR CATTLE BREEDS IN SCOTLAND

The cattle sector is the largest single contributor to Scottish farm output, amounting to around about half the total. It has a diversity of breeds contributing to its importance, and the top 10, according to Scottish Government figures, are:

1. Limousin: 378,000 or 21% of cattle in Scotland. Still at number one, this has been the longstanding favourite in Scotland, though numbers have fallen 28% since 2006.

2. Aberdeen Angus: quite a way behind at 279,000 or 15% of cattle. Moved up to second in 2007, overtaking both Simmental and Charolais in one go.

3. Simmental: 260,000 or 14% of cattle, not looking likely to catch Aberdeen Angus, with very steady numbers over the last decade.

4. Holstein Friesian: 246,000 or 14% of cattle. Overtook Charolais in 2010. Most popular dairy breed. Has been catching up with Simmental but whether it does will depend on the health of the dairy industry.

5. Charolais: 188,000 or 10% of cattle. Down from being second most popular in 2006, since when numbers have reduced by 29%.

6. Holstein: 68,000 or four per cent of cattle. There is a big gap between fifth and sixth place. Holsteins moved up one place in 2014 and have seen a 30% increase in numbers since 2006.

7. British Blue: 60,000 or three per cent of cattle. Dropped down one place in 2014 and has seen a 26% reduction in numbers since 2006.

8. British Friesian: 42,000 or two per cent. Has maintained eighth place with fairly steady numbers over the last decade.

9. Salers: 38,000 or two per cent of cattle. Moved up to ninth place in 2007, when it overtook the Blonde d'Aquitaine, a breed which has since plummeted to 19th. Salers have seen a 44% increase in numbers since 2006.

10. Beef Shorthorn: 32,000 or two per cent of cattle. Broke into the top ten only in 2015, replacing the Dual Shorthorn, and have seen numbers almost trebling since 2006.

RING WORK

Labour and machinery sharing co-operatives came over to Scotland from Germany in the 1980s. The concept is simple: a member with excess machinery or labour capacity hires the surplus out to a neighbour who requires help. Not long after they were established, the rings moved into supplying members' other needs such as fuels and fertilisers. The top ten services provided by Ringlink, whose 2,000 plus members stretch from the Moray Coast to the Tay, are:

1. Supply of labour
2. Tractor and driver
3. Road haulage
4. Supply of fuel
5. Supply of straw
6. Supply of feed barley/wheat
7. Supply of fertiliser
8. Supply of electricity
9. Land rentals
10. Training

These are mainstream requests but it has also had to deal with more challenging demands:

1. "Can you send someone to catch a tup which has outrun the vet and its owner?"
2. "The local rendering plant needs cleaning up."
3. "Can you organise the house clearance of someone who has deceased?"
4. "Can you supply bags for potato roguing?"
5. "Can you supply a wet suit for clearing a drain under a road?"
6. "We need a potato grading squad to go over to Jersey."
7. "Can you supply 50 trailers to protect soft fruit poly tunnels from the wind?"
8. "Can you send a man to watch a fire in a heap of smoking barley tonight?"
9. "Do you hire out tyres?"
10. "I am looking for six clay tiles."

One of the bugbears of those working in rings is the lack of forward planning…

1. "I need a tractor and driver yesterday."
2. "My grading staff has not turned up and I need replacements now."
3. Another of the same, with a phone call at lunchtime: "Can I get diesel this afternoon?"

4. An ominous threat: "Ye will hae to get kerosene for me the day or else the wife's moovin' oot."

And to prove their financial sharpness, the following comments have been collected:

1. "That's too dear I need a discount."
2. "Can I back date my membership to receive your discount?"
3. "Can I get your discount and the NFU discount too?"
4. Which only leaves: "That's too cheap I need to pay more."

'Can you supply a wet suit for clearing
a drain under a road?'

TEN AGRICULTURAL PARISHES
WITH THE LONGEST NAMES

1. **Broughton, Glenholm and Kilbucho (Parish code 635)** At 28 letters, the longest agricultural parish name in Scotland. It consists of 7,000 hectares of agricultural land in the Scottish Borders, not far to the east of Biggar; mainly rough grazing and grassland, supporting 27,000 sheep and 900 cattle.

2. **Glenmuick, Tullich and Glengairn (Parish code 43):** 27 letters. 21,000 hectares of agricultural land in Aberdeenshire, 12 miles east of Braemar; mainly rough grazing, with 10,000 sheep and 1,400 cattle.

3. **Anstruther Wester and Easter (Parish code 416):** 25 letters. Only 460 hectares of agricultural land along the south east coast of Fife; only a couple of holdings, but it is an excellent place to buy fish and chips. One of four parishes in the top ten with a reasonable amount of crops.

4. **Lochgoilhead and Kilmorich (Parish code 144):** 24 letters. 20,000 hectares to the north of Loch Long in Argyll. It is mainly rough grazing and woodland, primarily grazing sheep.

5. **Kilfinichen and Kilvickeon (Parish code 165):** 24 letters. About 20,000 hectares on holdings, plus about 3,000 hectares of common grazing, comprising the two south-western peninsulas of Mull. It is mainly rough grazing and woodland with 14,000 sheep and 1,000 cattle.

6. **Urquhart and Glenmoriston (Parish code 437):** 23 letters. More than 36,000 hectares on holdings and 1,500 hectares of common grazing, to the west of Loch Ness. It is nearly all rough grazing, woodland and grass, with 12,600 sheep and 1,600 cattle.

7. **Kilbrandon and Kilchattan (Parish code 172):** 23 letters. 7,000 hectares of mainly rough grazing, 10,000 sheep and 1,000 cattle. It consists of the islands of Seil, Luing, Shuna, and Torsa, together with a part of the neighbouring mainland.

8. **St Andrews and St Leonards (Parish code 431):** 22 letters. This is the one in Fife that includes St Andrews – there are two other parishes with St Andrews in their name, one in Orkney, one in Moray. More than half the farmland is growing cereals, but there are also 1,500 cattle and 2,500 sheep.

9. **Whitekirk and Tyninghame (Parish code 368):** 22 letters. 2,000 hectares of cereals, potatoes, veg, and some pigs, situated along the coast to the east of North Berwick, in East Lothian.

10. **Covington and Thankerton (Parish code 520):** 22 letters. Situated in South Lanarkshire, between Lanark and Biggar, it consists of 2,200 hectares of grass, rough grazing and cereals, with 5,000 sheep and 3,000 cattle.

BRITISH LIMOUSIN

From the initial import application back in the 1960s, followed by the few pioneers importing those cattle in 1971, the breed, which was largely unknown to UK farmers, has now become the foremost in the country. It has built its reputation on being 'The Carcase Breed', and is the largest numerical beef breed in the UK, accounting for well over a quarter of all cattle registered with the British Cattle Movement Service. Each year about 500,000 Limousin-sired cattle are registered, representing an annual industry value of around £600 million. It is further estimated that some 75% of all beef cattle in the UK carry a percentage of Limousin genetics.

TOP PRICED BRITISH LIMOUSIN BULLS SOLD AT AUCTION

1. **Trueman Jagger** – sold by H. Savage & Sons at Carlisle in 2015 for 140,000 guineas to a five-strong consortium made up of Mr and Mrs Alford, P. Dawes, Messrs Jenkinson, G. Lee and Kedzlie Farm.

2. **Dolcorsllwyn Fabio** – sold by G. and N. Vaughan at Carlisle in 2012 for 120,000gns to Messrs Jenkinson.

3. **Haltcliffe Vermont** – sold by Haltcliffe at Carlisle in 2006 for 100,000gns to Procters Farm.

4. **Ampertaine Mozart** – sold by J. McKay at Carlisle in 2017 for 100,000gns to Procters Farm.

5. **Haltcliffe DJ** – from Haltcliffe, sold at Carlisle in 2010 for 72,000gns jointly to Procters Farm and Nether Hall Farm.

6. **Wilodge Outlook** – from Wilodge Limousins, sold in Carlisle in 2017 for 60,000gns to Boden and Davies.

7. **Grahams Samson** – sold by R. and J. Graham at Carlisle in 2004 for 55,000gns to D.K. Wheeler.

8. **Queenshead Altea** – sold by P. and J. Varley at Carlisle in 2007 for 52,000gns to T. Bailey.

The top female price for the breed is for Glenrock Illusion, sold by Mr and Mrs Illingworth at Carlisle in 2016 for 125,00gns to Mr and Mrs Alford and Kedzlie Farm.

A second-top female price of 65,000gns was paid for Bankdale Erin, a heifer from G. Wilson, in Carlisle in 2011 by Procters Farm.

BEST HABITATS FOR WILDLIFE

1. Woods, trees and scrub – well-managed scrub and its margins supports a range of wildlife. It provides nectar, seeds, fruits, shelter and nest sites for invertebrates, birds and mammals. It also provides a suitable habitat for many flowering plants.

2. Hedges and ditches – provide a haven for many insects, wildflowers, small mammals, reptiles and amphibians. The best hedges are those with a good mixture of native species.

3. Wet features – such as farm ponds provide an important habitat for many species which live, feed or breed in or near water. Drainage channels can be important corridors that allow species to move through the countryside.

4. Flower-rich areas – provide nectar throughout spring and summer to supply food for insects such as butterflies and bumblebees. The best hay meadows are the product of traditional, low intensity farming.

5. Seed-rich areas – areas sown with wild bird seed mixtures provide vital food for seed-eating birds throughout winter. They are particularly important in areas where traditional food sources such as weedy stubbles and cereals fed to outdoor stock are no longer available.

6. Field margins – arable margins are generally the least productive areas of a field and just a one metre strip round a field can benefit wildlife in many ways. On grassland systems, a narrow strip can be allowed to go to seed and develop a structure that will be used by nesting birds and large, long-lived insects.

And on a grander scale…

1. Caledonian forest – 60% of the remaining Caledonian pine forests are found within the Cairngorms national park. These forests are essential for the survival of capercaillie, with more than 75% of the population found within forests in Strathspey.

2. The Flow Country of Caithness and Sutherland – one of Scotland's real treasures. It is the largest single expanse of blanket bog found anywhere in the world, with Scotland holding 13% of the world's blanket bog area. The bog acts as a massive carbon store and supports a wide range of wildlife.

3. Mountain heath and willow scrub – Scotland provides 98% of the UK total. Careful management of grazing animals encourages a range of rare invertebrate and plant species.

4. Machair – a very rare and special type of coastal grassland, with more than 70% of all the machair in the world found on the western coastline of the islands of the Hebrides. Machair farming systems support many priority wildlife species including corncrake, great yellow bumblebee, rare orchids and thousands of waders

SCOTTISH FARM INVENTORS

Sir Winston Churchill once said: "Of all the small nations of this earth, perhaps only the ancient Greeks surpass the Scots in their contribution to mankind." Proving that point, below find a few Scottish agricultural inventions:

1. Rev. Patrick Bell (1800-1869)
Invented the reaping machine. He was minister in Carmyllie parish in Angus and invented the earliest model of the binder on his father's farm. It ran on two wheels and was pushed by two horses.

2. Sir Hugh Dalrymple (1690-1755)
Invented an improved drainage system. A distinguished judge, he was also credited with inventing the hollow pipe system of land drainage.

3. Andrew Meikle (1852-1916)
A mechanical engineer credited with inventing the threshing machine. He worked as a millwright in East Linton, East Lothian. His father invented automatic grain fanners.

4. James Smith (1789–1850)
An agricultural engineer, initially a partner in Deanston cotton works, Perthshire. He turned his hand to various inventions, the most notable that of subsoiling. Using subsoiling at Deanston, land formerly overgrown with rushes, furze and broom was transformed into cultivated land.

5. James Porteus (1868–1922)
Born in Haddington and, after education, moved to America where he established a wagon-making shop in Tresno. There he invented the Tresno Scraper; a soil moving device for constructing ditches and canals. The design was revolutionary and economical. Its influence can still be seen in the design of modern bulldozer blades and earth movers.

6. Graham Tuley
A forester with the Forestry Commission UK, he invented the tree shelter, or tree guard, in 1979. Ten million guards were produced in 1991. They protect newly-planted trees from herbivores and herbicides.

7. James Small
Born in 1740 in the parish of Ladykirk, Berwickshire. Building on his experience of the Rotherham plough, he introduced the first plough in Scotland made of metal instead of wood. This was known as the swing plough or Scots plough and was more easily pulled with a pair of horse and one man rather than four horses or oxen and two men.

8. John Reekie (1910-2013)
Born in Angus and raised on his father's farm at Glamis. In the 1950s John developed a narrow tractor for use in the raspberry fields; the design was taken up by Ferguson and is still used worldwide in vineyards.

9. Robert Ewan
Reportedly from near Cupar, Fife, he invented the Dinkum Digger. This is the ditch-digging attachment fitted on the back of a tractor or, as the Americans call it, a back hoe. Whitlock Bros. from Essex bought the licence and built it commercially. It was then exported to Australia, hence the name.

10. Wull Scorgie and his late father, also Wull
Made one of the earliest usable stone separators, essential for mechanically lifted potatoes, at their smiddy at Balrownie, Brechin. The concept was also taken up by David Wilson, Balmullo, Fife who built two row models, the basis for those in use today.

BETTER FARMERS, BETTER COUNTRYMEN, BETTER CITIZENS

The slogan above was suggested by R.F. Gregor, the driving force behind the Scottish Association of Young Farmers Clubs for half a century. Just how the young farmers in the 1960s and 1970s aimed at such lofty ideals can be gleaned from some of the winter programmes for their clubs. For those Young Farmers brought up in the 1950s and 1960s where there was stockjudging, speechmaking and not much else, some of the following may seem a little exotic.

1. 'Split meetings' were quite common, with the boys hearing about something instructive relating to farming while the girls often had to make do with more domestic issues. Thus 'Boys will hear of crop diseases – every girl a diamond pleases' was a split meeting on crop diseases and jewellery (Perth and District JAC).

2. Jim Clark Memorial Programme – this aimed to help members equip themselves to make the best use of their leisure time. Named after a worthy world racing car champion and role model, this course – based on knowledge of cars – had a number of useful activities including fault-finding, repairs, maintenance, and especially useful for young farmers – night driving skills.

3. Personality programme – this aimed to help members equip themselves to lead a fuller and better life in an age when many of the finer arts had tended to become neglected. The section on 'Behaviour' included 'Everyday Manners' – at the table, answering the telephone and answering the door.

4. Another split meeting, but with a bit more gender equality from Arbroath and District JAC; Boys – 'Survival' – Simple repairs to clothes including darning and patching; Girls – 'Top to Toe' – Hair care.

5. 'Design for Living' – this programme set out to help members enjoy a fuller life by including others in their design for living. In section one, there were courses on 'Boyfriends, Fiancees and Husbands.' There were no proficiency tests in this section.

6. 'Let's have a Party' – to encourage members in groups to appreciate the value of good planning and organisation of social functions. One part included 'How do I keep my cool? – Introductions, etiquette and conversation'.

7. Less innocent times – a talk to Atholl JAC from the Family Planning Clinic and to Aberfeldy and District JAC on glue sniffing and drug abuse.

8. In the mid-seventies there was a craze for setting out the winter programme in verse or catchy titles, so Teviotdale YFC had 'Eeny Meeny Minny Mooo' dairy stockjudging for the boys and a 'Quiche Lorraine' competition for the girls. Back to gender stereotyping again.

9. 'Know your Countryside' – a competition to stimulate awareness of and interest in the effects of modern farming trends and techniques on the amenity and wildlife of the countryside. Way before its time and before this became a burning issue.

10. 'Efficiency with Safety Competition' – the aim was to stimulate an awareness and interest in the need for safe practice in agriculture among young farmers, and to encourage skill and efficiency on the farm. Tasks included operating a fork lift, coupling implements and driving a tractor and trailer safely. Although essential, this mustn't have been popular since it only appeared once.

'Survival' and 'Top to Toe'

. . . better darners, better hairdressers

FARM INSURANCE CLAIMS

With more than 300 local offices over the UK, NFU Mutual insures over three-quarters of the nation's farmers. Based on its claims experience, the most commonly stolen items from farms are:

1. Tools – not surprising this is number one as small tools are easy to lift and easy to sell on for cash.

2. Oil/diesel – a potential thief needs to be well-organised to pilfer this commodity in bulk.

3. Machinery – often stolen to order. A certain amount of organisation is needed by the miscreants before nicking heavy items.

4. Garden equipment – we are constantly reminded to lock up our garden sheds, but there is a big market for mowers, hedge trimmers, strimmers and all garden tools.

5. Livestock – this offence comes on two levels. The first being the chance capture and slaughter of an animal. The second is the more organised thefts by gangs armed with livestock transport and dogs.

6. Vehicles – cars, pick-ups and ATVs are easy to drive away and are often left in farm yards with their ignition keys in place.

7. Metal – scrap and not so scrap used to find a ready market for cash, but now scrap metal dealers are being discouraged from paying cash, this crime is less attractive.

8. Tractors – while it is hard to believe that they would be stolen on chance, there is a ready market in some foreign countries.

9. Trailers – even more organisation needed here, as a tractor or truck is needed to pull them. But there are quite sophisticated and expensive trailers and horse boxes out there and the criminal fraternity see them as easy pickings.

CHAPTER TEN

THE 10 MOST POPULAR CROPS GROWN IN SCOTLAND

1. Barley – 286,930 hectares, 40% of which is grown in Grampian. Scotland's most popular farm crop, covering 49% of the country's crop area. More than four fifths of it is spring-sown. Most barley is used for animal feed, but a lot is used in the whisky and beer industry. Worth about £180 million in 2016, barley accounted for about 6% of output from farms.

2. Wheat – 109,594 hectares or 19% of crop area. The value of the wheat crop has averaged about £115m in recent years, mainly used in the whisky industry and as animal feed.

3. Oats – 31,210 hectares with three quarters being spring-sown. Was once Scotland's main crop. Has seen a resurgence in recent years, with 2016 seeing the second highest area and the highest yield since the 1970s. Oats now account for 5% of crop area.

4. Oilseed – 30,731 hectares. Responsible for turning large swathes of the country yellow each spring, particularly in Grampian which grows about a third of the crop. Nearly all of it is winter-sown.

5. Potatoes – 27,525 hectares, including about 13,000 hectares growing certified seed potatoes. The ware crop is worth about £125m while the seed crop is worth about £70m. We produce more than 1.1m tonnes of potatoes, about half of them in Tayside.

6. Peas for human consumption – 7,540 hectares, of which 65% are grown in Tayside. The crop is valued at about £12m.

7. Turnips/swedes for stockfeed – 4,099 hectares, half of which are in Grampian.

8. Rye – 3,725 hectares. Probably used mainly in anaerobic digestion plants nowadays, it has seen a large increase in recent years.

9. Carrots – 3,252 hectares, with Tayside and Grampian producing two thirds. The 190,000 tonne crop is valued at about £30m.

10. Beans for combining – 3,002 hectares, a third of which are in the Scottish Borders. Fed as a protein crop to livestock.

10 SCOTTISH GOVERNMENT FORMS

1. June Agricultural Census: Comes in two varieties; the long form that collects the full range of crops, livestock and workforce data, completed by 10,000 smaller holdings who don't complete a SAF, and the short form completed by 23,000 SAF applicants, as their crop data is taken from their SAF.

2. Single Application Form: The Gateway to Funding. Completed by 20,000 businesses, and mostly completed in its online version, although about 5,000 businesses still use paper. Commonly referred to as the SAF.

3. December Agricultural Survey: Collects data on rent levels, winter plantings, livestock numbers and machinery, and sent to a sample of about 15,000 larger holdings. Available online since 2015.

4. Farm Structure and Practices Survey: This one occurs only every three or four years, and is mainly driven by the EU. Collects more detailed data on the workforce, together with data on diversification and agricultural practices, and is sent to a sample of about 15,000 larger holdings.

5. Annual Sheep and Goat Inventory: Does what it says on the tin, collecting sheep and goat numbers. Sent to all sheep and goat keepers, unless they are already receiving a December Agricultural Survey, so about 10,000 keepers. Available online since 2015.

6. Hours and Earnings Survey: Sent to a sample of 650 holdings who have recorded employing workers in their most recent June Census. Used to estimate the cost of labour to farming, as part of the national accounts.

7. Cereal Production and Disposal Survey: Sent to a sample of about 600 holdings, you only see this if you're a cereal producer. Gives an estimate of the cereal harvest and what grain has been used for, and feeds into the national accounts.

8. Monthly Milk Price and Utilisation Form: Sent to the seven large dairies on a monthly basis and 19 smaller ones on a quarterly basis. Also has an annual version that provides more detailed breakdown of usage.

9. Slaughter Statistics: Sent in by Scotland's 19 abattoirs, providing slaughter numbers and average weights on a weekly basis.

10. Bank Advances Survey: Annual collection of the amount of loans to Scottish agriculture, sent to 11 banks.

TOP ABERDEEN ANGUS

The Aberdeen Angus heyday in the late 1950s and early 1960s saw American and Argentinian buyers beat a path to the Perth bull sales each year to snap up the top bulls at extortionate prices. A new record price was set every year for four years between 1960 and 1963 – in 1962 the record was broken twice at the same sale – and continued until 1967 when prices began to ease. This coincided with a change in market demand world-wide towards a larger animal compared with the small 'dumpy' type of Aberdeen-Angus which had been popular until then. British breeders were slow to change and the breed declined rapidly through the 1970s and 1980s, but made a huge recovery from the 1990s onwards as Aberdeen-Angus beef gained greater public recognition and supermarkets started paying a premium for the cattle. In recent years, prices for bulls have not returned to the dizzy heights of the 1960s but a strong demand for breeding stock has resulted in record prices for females of the breed.

TOP PRICED BULLS

1. 60,000gns in 1963 for Lindertis Evulse from Sir Torquil Munro to Black Watch Farms, New York.

2. 54,000gns in 1964 for Essedium of Douneside from MacRobert Farms to Black Watch Farms, New York.

3. 40,000gns in 1965 for Erisco of Ballechin from Miss Elizabeth Honeyman to Black Watch Farms, New York.

4. 38,000gns in 2006 for Cardona Jewel Eric D276 from Ian and Robbie Galloway to David Walker.

5. 34,000gns in 1965 for Newhouse Jarvis Eric from Mrs Ann Adam to Black Watch Farms, New York.

6. 33,000gns in 1963 for Jumbos Eric of Candacraig from Mrs A.F. Wallace to Mario Hirsch/Antony Leloir, Argentina.

7. 30,000gns in 2006 for The Moss Mr Eshton D409 from John Moores to W. and D. McLaren/W. Porter and Son.

8. 29,200gns in 1961 for Evril of Wandel from Walter Ross-Taylor to R.M. Adam and Son.

9. 28,000gns in 1961 for Newhouse Jewror Eric from R.M. Adam and Son to Keith Bromley/H.M. Gold.

10. 28,000gns in 2000 for Jeremy Eric of Bridgefoot from A. Fordyce and Sons to Alistair Fraser.

11. 27,000gns in 1960 for Newhouse Jewbilee Eric from R.M. Adam and Son to Charles Clore.

TOP PRICED FEMALES

1. 35,000gns in 2016 for Blelack Lady Eraline J258 from N.F. Massie and Sons to Balavil Estate.

2. 32,000gns in 2012 for Blelack Eyrie G197 from N.F. Massie and Sons to John Loftus.

3. 30,000gns in 2007 for Netherton Missie A114 from W. and D. McLaren to John Lascelles.

4. 24,000gns in 2012 for Rawburn Edith K180 from John Elliot to Ben Marsden.

5. 20,000gns in 2004 for Netherton Fleur Y298 from W. and D. McLaren to Scottish Coal Co.

6. 16,000gns in 2004 for Kim of Fordafourie from W. and D. McLaren/R. and D. Orr to John Lascelles.

7. 16,000gns in 2004 for Netherton Missie Y288 from W. and D. McLaren to Bryan Ronan.

TOP OF THE TREES

Scotland has lots of fantastic forests and woodlands, set in some of the most picturesque areas of the country. Below is a selection of the best as supplied by Confor, the industry's representative body.

10 AWARD-WINNING WOODS

Community woodlands of different sizes and compositions are growing in popularity along with native woodland creation programmes. The woods named here were some of the winners and runners up in the 2017 Scotland's Finest Woods Awards, and represent hard work by many people over many years to achieve the results now visible. At Jerah, the largest modern planting site in Scotland, 1.3 million trees were planted in 2015 to provide a significant future timber crop and deliver a range of public benefits, including encouraging biodiversity, reducing flood risks and enhancing public access.

1. Jerah, Sherrifmuir, Dunblane (Quality timber)

2. Underbank primary school, South Lanarkshire (Schools)

3. Airor common grazings native woodland, Knoydart (Large community woodland)

4. Doune Ponds, Perthshire (Small community woodland group)

5. Carrifran Wildwood, Moffat Hills (New native woods)

6. Mar Lodge Estate pinewoods, Braemar (New native woods)

7. Camis Eskan, Helensburgh (Quality timber)

8. Wild Willows, Kincraig (Schools)

9. Aigas community forest, Inverness-shire (Large community woodland)

10. Falkland Estate, Fife (Large community woodland)

TEN OF SCOTLAND'S MOST BEAUTIFUL FORESTS TO VISIT

There aren't many other crops which double as tourist attractions, but many of Scotland's forests have walking trails, mountain bike routes, wildlife hides, archaeological sites, sculptures, and even visitor centres, treetop assault courses and music festivals. You don't have to walk far into any forest, though, to leave all the bustle behind and enjoy some of the most peaceful places in Scotland.

1. Faskally wood, Perthshire

2. Abriachan forest, Highlands

3. Rothiemurchus forest, Aviemore

4. Glen Affric, Cannich

5. Great Forest of Loch Ard, Aberfoyle

6. Loch Loyne forest parks

7. Wood of Cree, Galloway

8. Craigvinean forest, Dunkeld

9. Glentress forest, Peebles

10. Cawdor Castle forest, Nairnshire

BEST EXAMPLES OF USING WOOD
IN NEW SCOTTISH TIMBER BUILDINGS

There's something delightful about timber buildings, and every timber building began life in a forest somewhere. Here are ten of our favourite modern Scottish timber buildings, many of them recent winners of the Wood for Good and Forestry Commission Award for the best use of timber:

1. The Inn at John O'Groats

2. Edinburgh Centre for Carbon Innovation

3. Raasay village hall

4. House at Camusdarrach Sands

5. House No.7, Tiree

6. 3 Old Orchard, Dundee

7. Helix Café pavilion, Falkirk

8. SNH headquarters, Inverness

9. Ben Wyvis primary school, Conon Bridge

10. South Doll farmhouse, by Airth

CARTOON CHARACTERS

An amazing number of cartoon characters have their origins in the farmyard. Among the most famous are:

1. Peppa Pig (first appeared, 2004)
Sorry Porky fans, but there's only room on this list for one hog, and the sassy (some might even say bratty) Peppa absolutely insisted it was her. Not even the world-famous Miss Piggy, who appeared in cartoon form in 'Muppet Babies', can barge her way in. The adventures of Peppa – along with friends such as Suzy Sheep, Pedro Pony and Danny Dog – have been charming children around the world since 2004, but what makes the show a particularly rare breed is its ability to appeal to adults as well.

2. Foghorn Leghorn (1946)
Based on Senator Claghorn, the popular 1940s radio character, Foghorn Leghorn was a Southern rooster who was loud, obnoxious and – randomly – once cited by former Scotland goalkeeper Jim Leighton as his favourite cartoon character. He was given his distinctive 'Ah say, boy' tones by the legendary Mel Blanc, the 'Man of 1,000 voices', which leads us nicely to the next entry on our list.

3. Bugs Bunny (1938)
Okay, so a rabbit isn't technically a farmyard animal, but Bugs is worthy of inclusion for giving us one of TV's most memorable catchphrases: 'What's up, doc?' How many people can honestly say they've chomped on a raw carrot without uttering this immortal line? Such is the star quality of Elmer Fudd's nemesis that he even commanded top billing over basketball legend Michael Jordan in 1996's *Space Jam*. Not bad for a wascally wabbit.

4. Donald Duck (1934)
This was a close-run thing with Daffy, but the Disney waterfowl with the speech impediment beat his Loony Toons counterpart to our screens by three years. Bad tempered, difficult to understand but loveable nonetheless, Donald remains a popular figure on Disney TV shows and in its theme parks to this day. He's also notable for being one of the few ducks to help with the war effort, with his 1943 propaganda film, *Der Fuehrer's Face*, even bagging an Oscar. Eat your heart out, Mickey Mouse.

5. Ermintrude (1964)
One of the many memorable characters from the Sixties sensation, *The Magic Roundabout*, Ermintrude was a pink cow who wore a hat and spoke like Noel Coward. Along with Dougal the dog, Brian the snail, Dylan the rabbit and Zebedee the, erm, jack-in-the-box, Ermintrude's psychedelic adventures were considered unmissable television for children and adults alike. But even in the drug-fuelled era of the 1960s, there's nothing to be read

into the fact that Ermintrude enjoyed flying a kite after grazing on poppies. Nothing at all.

6. Shaun the Sheep (1995)

Spin-off series can go one of two ways – the way of *Frasier*, whose character went on to far greater things following the end of *Cheers*, or the way of *Joey*, whose post-*Friends* appearances are probably best forgotten. *Shaun the Sheep* managed to upstage both Wallace and Gromit in 1995's *A Close Shave* with his adorable antics and was given his own eponymous series in 2007. After 150 episodes, a hit feature film (with another in the pipeline) and even a spin-off of his own – *Timmy Time* – it's fair to say Shaun falls firmly into the former category.

7. Donkey (2001)

Eddie Murphy has given cinemagoers plenty of laughs over the years, from *Beverley Hills Cop* and *Trading Places* to *Coming to America* and *The Nutty Professor*, but perhaps none have given more joy than his scene-stealing vocal performances in the *Shrek* movies. Quite simply, Donkey is the character Murphy was born to play, even earning him a BAFTA nomination for Best Supporting Actor. His line about "making waffles" alone should have won him the gong.

8. Black Bob (1944)

A popular character in *The Dandy* for nearly 40 years, illustrator Jack Prout's Black Bob is probably the second most famous Border Collie in the world, behind a certain Lassie. If imitation is the sincerest form of flattery, Selkirk-born Bob would be delighted to see his adventures with shepherd Andrew Glen parodied by adult comic *Viz* with its tales of Black Bag, the Faithful Border Binliner.

9. Maximus (2010)

On seeing the name Maximus, you may well find yourself thinking that, while Russell Crowe has a certain animalistic quality – not least in his name – he's not a cartoon character. That's because this Maximus is the sword-wielding horse from smash-hit Disney animation *Tangled*, who was named in honour of the Oscar-winning Aussie's character in *Gladiator*. The mission of this Maximus isn't to dish out vengeance, but to provide mirth, which he does neigh bother (sorry).

10. Emperor Kuzco (2000)

The star of *The Emperor's New Groove* actually starts out as a human, albeit a narcissistic, arrogant one. It's only when his former advisor Yzma (voiced with delicious menace by the legendary Eartha Kitt) turns him into a llama and he has to rely on one of his poor subjects that he begins to see the error of his ways. An underrated – and often hilarious – addition to Disney's collection of animated classics.

HEADGEAR SEEN IN THE COUNTRYSIDE

Increasingly country roads are becoming filled with cycle helmets of various shapes and sizes in all the colours of the rainbow, but other headgear can be spotted in the countryside by the eagle-eyed.

1. The cap, or **bunnet** – part of the rite of passage for a boy brought up on the farm. Once the uniform of the working class, it's now popular with fashionistas of both sexes as well as being essential when standing around the Clydesdale judging ring or attending roups. Two rules for bunnet wearers are not too small and not too floppy.

2. The deerstalker – popular in green and brown tweed, the look is completed with a Norfolk jacket and a pair of plus fours. Immortalised by both Elmer Fudd and Sherlock Holmes, it is also known as 'fore and aft' on account of the brim front and back. Ear flaps are traditionally worn up but on bleak days on the hills, this favoured headgear for gamekeepers and ghillies is worn with flaps down.

3. Tam o'Shanter or tammy – a flat bonnet with a 'toorie' on the top. The hero of Robert Burns' poem embodies the stereotypical Scot – hard drinking, moralistic, superstitious and mawkish.

4. Baseball cap – popular on the farm as a walking advert for fertilisers, animal health products and tractors. They are also popular with those political enthusiasts who want to publicly say Yes or No or In or Out.

5. Straw hat – they offer valuable protection from both the sun and heatstroke which is seldom a problem for those living north of the Great Glen.

6. Beanie – this soft cloth pull-on hat which is the antidote to fashion is popular with walkers and foolhardy cyclists alike. Removing a beanie can result in static electricity causing spiky hair. This is not a problem for baldies.

7. Bucket hat or Sou' Wester – with gills for ventilation, waterproof capacity and the ability to slip into a poacher's pocket, the bucket hat provides the enthusiastic fisherman with perfect headgear. Also popular with vegetable pickers who have to work in the worst of weather.

8. Stetson – perfect for those who venture into the countryside looking for a John Wayne or a Clint Eastwood experience or for impressing others at bull sales. Etiquette requires that the stetson must be tight enough not to blow off your head; but not so tight as to leave a ring around your head.

9. The midgie net – time to put away Avon's Skin So Soft and the citronella candles. The midgie net not only provides you with a "Government expert on chemical warfare look" but makes the midgie have a second look too.

10. And finally, the **knotted hankie**. Now out of fashion, but then this do-it-yourself attempt at keeping the sun off the bald head was never in fashion.

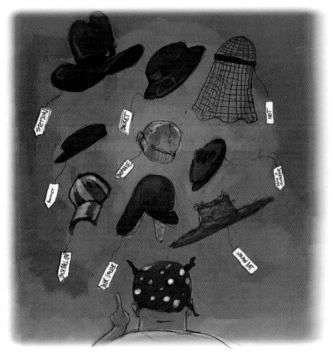

Stetson, bucket, midgie net, bunnet, beanie, tammy, baseball cap, straw hat and knotted hankie

'Which one today?'

DANGERS IN THE COUNTRYSIDE

Danger lurks in the countryside, with both plants and animals having the ability to harm humans, according to the website enjoythecountryside.com. Its dangerous top eight are:

1. Spiders – there are more than 650 different species in the UK – and all of them bite. Luckily, bites from spiders in the UK are rare. Only 12 of these species have enough venom that can cause harm to a human, but a few, such as the false widow spider, are capable of giving a nasty bite.

2. Ticks – at least eight people in Britain catch Lyme disease from a tick bite every day. Ticks are almost certainly the most dangerous bugs in the UK. You are more likely to get bitten by a tick than by a venomous snake, and the illnesses they spread can sometimes become life-threatening and have lifelong after-effects.

3. Wasps – more readily aggressive than bees and they can sting multiple times without dying. They will take great interest in any sugary food or drinks you take outside with you. They will also be attracted to your perfumed shampoo, washing powder or make-up.

4. Adders – the last time someone in Britain died from an adder bite was more than 20 years ago. They will only use their venom as a last means of defence, usually if caught or trodden on. Adders are relatively common in areas of rough, open countryside and are often associated with woodland edge habitats.

5. Cows – some people are unaware that cows can very aggressive in spring and summer when they have calves to protect, and that cows will stampede as a herd if they feel any of their number is in danger. More people have been killed by cows in Britain than by bulls.

6. Deer – aggressive and potentially dangerous animals, in all seasons. The females are very aggressive when they have fawns, from spring through the summer. The males are particularly aggressive during the rutting season, from October to December, and their testosterone-crazed behaviour can be completely irrational.

7. Horseflies or clegs – have sharp cutting parts which can saw through even the skin of an ox, and then drink the blood from their wound. The female's bites are extremely painful. Since ancient Greek times, they have featured in literature as being able to torment people to insanity. Luckily in Britain they do not spread any dangerous diseases, but their bites can still become infected and cause very nasty reactions.

8. Nettles – one of the most widespread plants in the UK, stinging nettles are the bane of many a country walk. Their leaves are covered in tiny, needle-like hairs. When you brush against a nettle, the hairs break off, penetrate your skin and sting you, producing the familiar burning sensation, itch and rash. The rash is very painful and usually lasts for several days.

THE 10 LOCAL AUTHORITIES
WITH THE MOST SHEEP PER PERSON

1. Shetland Islands – with 279,943 sheep (4% of Scotland's total) and only 23,200 people, sheep outnumber people by twelve to one. There are just under 500 sheep per square mile, the third highest density in Scotland.

2. Scottish Borders – more sheep than any other local authority; the 1,155,449 sheep and 114,530 people mean sheep outnumber people by ten to one. There are 630 sheep per square mile, the highest density in Scotland, accounting for 17% of Scotland's sheep.

3. Dumfries and Galloway – the only other local authority with more than a million sheep, with 1,062,843 or 16% of Scotland's sheep. With 149,520 people that makes a ratio of seven to one. There are 430 sheep per square mile.

4. Na h-Eileanan Siar or Western Isles – it has 148,874 sheep, but with only 26,900 people there are six times as many sheep as people. There are 130 sheep per square mile, the fifth lowest in Scotland.

5. Orkney Islands – more of a cattle island, the 117,514 sheep are less than 2% of Scotland's total, but with 21,850 people that gives a ratio of five to one. There are about 310 sheep per square mile.

6. Argyll & Bute – there are 426,336 sheep and 87,130 people, that's five times as many sheep as people. There are 160 sheep per square mile, fewer than in Edinburgh.

7. Highland – with 880,379 sheep and 234,770 people (the biggest population in our top ten), that makes four sheep per person. It has 13% of Scotland's sheep, but the vast expanses of the Highlands mean a density of only 90 sheep per square mile, the fourth lowest density in Scotland behind Aberdeen, Glasgow and Dundee.

8. Perth and Kinross – its 498,116 sheep and 150,680 people give it a ratio of three to one.

9. Stirling – 224,550 sheep and 93,750 people, so just over twice as many sheep as people.

10. South Ayrshire – 222,837 sheep and 112,470 people, giving just under twice as many sheep as people. It does have, though, the fourth highest density of sheep, at 470 per square mile.

THE SOURCES OF FARMING FAMILY ARGUMENTS

A family working farm provides a fair number of flashpoints. The following list has been contributed by some who have been there and, using a cliché, have the T-shirt to prove it.

1. Moving cattle/sheep – stressful at the best of times and where faults can lead to tempers being lost. Examples are; standing in the wrong place, coming forward too quickly, coming forward too slowly. In summary, the gate filler gets the blame if the livestock escape.

2. Tipping grain – at busy harvest times, inexperienced amateur tractor drivers who are often junior family members are enlisted to help bring the harvest home. They often forget to secure the back door before driving off, leaving a trail of grain which looks much worse than it is.

3. Failing to switch the electric fence back on – animals are not as stupid as they are portrayed and they learn when the fence is not live just as quickly as they learn when it is live.

4. Buying expensive machinery or livestock without telling anyone – many farm businesses are partnerships or limited companies and big purchases should be discussed before the event and not after. A regular occurrence during the sale season and when roups are held.

5. Covering the silage pit – negotiating polythene sheeting and old, dirty tyres into their place requires co-ordination and even tempers. These are not always achieved.

6. Trying to be cheerful at a critical point in harvest when the combine has broken down or when the rain has arrived before forecast is not always appreciated.

7. Wrong spare part – when the gofer arrives back home after an hour's visit to the machinery dealers with the wrong part it is not his/her fault that the serial number has been forgotten. It is no good explaining the storeman should have known the correct part needed.

8. Mealtimes ignored – of course work on the farm outside the farmhouse is more important than work inside, but meat and two veg isn't improved by sitting in the oven for two hours.

9. Equal status – when two or more members of the family have equal status in running the business, arguments are bound to happen.

10. Second business – many farms have a related business to complement the main farming enterprise. They often fit well; machinery contracting and farm shops come to mind, but there is potential for conflict, however, when two enterprises require labour or machinery at the same time.

Tipping Grain

'It was full when I left the field . . .'

STEAM PLOUGHING ENGINES AND MAKERS

One of the most important agricultural innovations in the nineteenth century was steam ploughing and cultivation. From the late 1850s Scottish farmers could choose engines and tackle from a number of makers.

1. John Fowler & Co (Leeds) Ltd, Leeds, was the most eminent ploughing engine and tackle maker and a household name around the world. By the 1870s most of the engines in Scotland were of Fowler manufacture, using the double engine system.

2. J. & F. Howard, Bedford, was a leading maker of ploughing engines and tackle from the early 1860s. Its 'Farmer's engine' was one of the most popular ploughing engines. Howard was better-known for its ploughs and wide-range of implements.

3. Fisken & Co Ltd, Leeds, included members of the Fisken family, of Drumphin, parish of Fowlis Wester, Perthshire, whose balance plough was adopted by John Fowler & Co. The Fisken tackle, on the endless rope system, was a popular system in Scotland.

4. Barrows & Carmichael, Banbury, was a maker of ploughing engines from 1864-66, before focusing on the second-hand market for ploughing tackle and traction engines.

5. J. & H. McLaren, Leeds, a well-known traction engine maker from 1876, whose family were from Overardock, Perthshire, was one of the most celebrated makers of ploughing engines. It continued to advertise its engines and tackle to Scottish farmers in the early 1920s, in competition against the newly emerging tractors.

6. Clayton & Shuttleworth, Lincoln, manufactured Fowler engines under licence in 1862. It was better known for its traction engines and threshing machines.

7. Richard Garrett & Son, Suffolk, manufactured Fowler engines under licence in 1864, also bringing them to the attention of Scottish farmers in the agricultural press in that year.

8. Aveling & Porter, Rochester, was one of the smaller makers of ploughing engines, manufacturing them from 1868 to early 1880s. It was a regular attender at the Royal Show between 1873 to 1883, but only attended the Highland Show in 1882. It was also well known for its agricultural locomotives, road locomotives and road rollers.

9. Barford & Perkins, Peterborough, started manufacturing ploughing engines in 1874. It continued to advertise them to Scottish farmers until 1885. It exhibited one at the Highland Show in 1877, also arranging a trial on a nearby farm.

10. F. Savage, King's Lynn, a maker of traction engines, developed its ploughing engine in 1872. However, it was not until 1876 that it sold its first one in Scotland, at Hermiston. It continued to advertise them in the Scottish agricultural press until 1879.

CHAPTER ELEVEN

Make them into handbags

Some ideas are better than others

USES OF WELLY BOOTS

It was 'big city' boy and comedian, Billy Connelly, who popularised the wearing of welly boots. Traditionally wellies were black, but nowadays they come in all colours regardless of the fashion statement they are or are not making. They are there to keep feet dry but wearers end up with soggy feet from perspiration. When they cease to keep the wet out, they can be put to other uses:

1. Make fun wellie plant pots – drill holes in the soles if they are not already leaky, then fill up with compost and plant. Ideal for trailing plants.

2. Make them into handbags – if you are desperate for something to be eye catching and also to go with your new attire, cut away the sole and make an unique handbag.

3. Wellie throwing competitions – these are keenly contested at local gala days and the organisers often need a supply of used wellies for the competitors.

4. Doorstop – if you are either a real cheapskate or are in the forefront of fashion, get your old wellies, then fill them with sand and use them as doorstops.

5. Christmas present – for the desperate last minute shopper or those with a Machiavellian mind. They should be smelt before wrapping.

6. Waterproof clogs – if perchance, the holes are in the upper part of the welly, this part can be cut off, leaving a serviceable pair of waterproof clogs.

7. Shed storage wellies – for storing all the little things in the garden shed that you no longer need but won't throw out.

8. Umbrella stand – again one for the cheapskates. Fill base with sand to provide stability.

9. Chicken feeder – cut the top of the toe section away and hey presto, you have a readymade feeder for the chickens.

10. Hobby horse – for the technically advanced. Insert broom handle into welly and fashion a mane and face.

IT IS IN THE FARM PICK-UP

The farm pick-up or van is a mobile workshop – of the roughest kind. It is also a store for medicines on livestock farms, carries bags of feed and mineral licks and an array of used containers. Beyond that it often carries both the essentials that might someday be needed such as fence wire and drain pipes, but also many assorted items that were needed in times past.

1. Baler twine – not as common now that small bales are less common but handy to have some on hand for the many uses of this commodity.

2. Several pocket knives – for use on the above, none of which can be found when most needed, and none sharp.

3. A shifter – which rattles around the footwell but is left there as it 'could come in handy'.

4. The remnants of an elderly pack of Polos – not recommended for consumption.

5. Some electric fencing insulators – most likely broken.

6. *Readers Digest* UK road map 1985 issue – just in case there's ever a chance the truck ventures further than usual.

7. Baseball cap – freebie from a farm supply company which neither fits nor is stylish but 'might be useful on a sunny/wet day'.

8. Tupperware box – with an ill-fitting lid from yesterday's afternoon fly-cup.

9. Elderly chamois leather – for clearing the windows after a wet day working outside.

10. Screwdriver – allowed to stay in the van for same reason as the shifter.

11. A small dead animal – not a permanent passenger.

12. £2.76 in loose change – not all in one place and not enough to buy the much needed fish supper or packet of cigarettes.

13. An almost-empty bottle of penicillin and a syringe with a broken needle – equally useless.

14. Keel stick – half used.

15. Barley samples – not necessarily from this harvest.

16. Empty soft drink cans – better here than thrown out the window.

17. Work-glove – but only one, naturally.

FARMING, FORESTRY AND WILDLIFE

REASONS TO HAVE TREES ON A FARM

Historically, farming and forestry have been two very separate industries in Scotland. But as farmers seek to diversify and look for solutions to environmental challenges, trees are becoming a more attractive option – and government policy has been making it easier. Here are ten reasons why planting trees on your farm could be healthy, wealthy and wise:

1. Tree shelter saves money by being able to keep animals outside with less food for more of the year.

2. Trees sequester carbon so your business can become carbon-negative.

3. Well-planted trees stop soil erosion and reduce drought and flooding.

4. Timber is a valuable crop which doesn't rely on subsidies.

5. Within a few years you will be able to harvest thinnings for firewood to use or sell.

6. Free-range livestock and poultry are less stressed and exhibit more natural behaviour when provided with tree cover.

7. Trees are beautiful.

8. Forestry comes with fencing grants, so forest structuring can also create improved pasture structuring.

9. Create wildlife habitat without losing productivity.

10. It will be a great place for your children and grandchildren to go mountain biking.

WILDLIFE WHICH LOVES PRODUCTIVE FORESTS

Scottish forests provide habitat for all kinds of wildlife, and well-managed productive forests are often better than dense, unmanaged woodland. Here are a few of the iconic and special species which live in the woods.

1. Scottish wildcat – hunts in clearfell and young plantations, shelters in full-grown forest, and nests in brash piles or under tree roots.

2. Capercaillie – once extinct due to the decline of its native woodland habitat, our iconic grouse was reintroduced to Britain from Europe in 1837.

3. Red squirrel – this species' ability to thrive in conifers better than greys allowed it to survive the grey invasion. Now, if you are lucky enough to live in a red squirrel protect zone, you will be able to grow quality hardwood, which in much of the UK is too badly damaged by greys.

4. Scottish crossbill – the only vertebrate species found exclusively in the UK, lives only in conifer woods.

5. Twinflower – a rare and delicate flower of Scottish pinewoods.

6. Hen harrier – following its extermination from mainland Scotland in the nineteenth century, the creation of conifer plantations gave this raptor the opportunity to return.

7. Short-eared owls – thrive on the prey to be hunted in young forests for the first twelve years after planting.

8. Bluebells – bluebells in the open, or among bracken, are a sign of 'ghost' woodland, a great place to plant trees. They need well-managed woodlands to thrive.

9. Songbirds – species which are declining in many places in Britain, such as willow warblers and meadow pipits, love newly-planted conifer habitats and their associated broadleaf planting; while song thrushes, crested tits, siskins, goldcrests and woodcock live in mature stands.

10. Rare butterflies and moths – species such as Chequered skipper, Kentish glory, and Pearl-bordered fritillary thrive in young woodlands and along woodland edges.

UNUSUAL ANIMALS BEING FARMED

Over hundreds of years, UK farmers have largely farmed four main species; cattle, sheep, pigs and poultry. This past century has seen more diversification, with a wide range of other animals living down on the farm. Among the more exotic livestock that have made an appearance on Scottish farms are:

1. Worms – vermiculture to use its proper name. Worm farming can be used to produce compost from waste or for live bait for anglers. Worm farms are often small, but there is a ten acre one in Dumfries.

2. Ostriches – multi-purpose birds supplying meat, leather and feathers. There are estimated to be about 100 ostrich farmers, or ranchers, in the UK. Female ostriches lay up to 50 eggs per annum but they do like a nice dry nesting area. Otherwise they tend to lay their eggs from a standing position. This can result in a big scrambled egg. Potential farmers are warned ostriches need a two metre high fence. They can also run at up to 40 miles per hour and deliver a very hard kick.

3. Alpacas – although they are used primarily as pack animals in their native South America, alpacas in the UK are farmed for their high quality fibre. Though they look very cuddly, they do have the ability to spit at humans who come too close.

4. Rabbits – farmed for their meat. Rabbit farming is small scale in the UK compared with Europe where more than 300 million are raised and slaughtered annually. SRUC provides estimates of costs of setting up a rabbit meat producing enterprise. There was a boom in farming Angora rabbits for their wool in the middle of last century.

5. Mink – when wearing fur was fashionable, mink farming was popular. Animal welfare enthusiasts objected to livestock being bred solely for fur and a law was passed banning this. Unfortunately, by the time the politicians acted, a number of mink had either escaped or had been released into the wild by the aforementioned animal welfare enthusiasts.

6. Silver fox – another species brought in after World War II to meet the demand for fur coats but which failed to survive when fashion changed.

7. Buffalo – thanks to the entrepreneurial approach of one or two farmers, a large number of people have now tasted and enjoyed buffalo burgers. In South East Asia, the homeland of buffalo, they are used to work in the fields and produce milk.

8. Wild boar – SRUC reckons there are an estimated 2,000 breeding wild boar sows on 30 farms in Scotland. Beyond these numbers, there are uncounted numbers in some of Scotland's remote wooded areas where they can cause surprise when startled by an unwary walker. Those on farms are kept for their meat.

UNWANTED PHONE CALLS

One of the curses of today is the unwanted phone call, with the caller wanting you to answer 'one or two questions' or sell you double glazing. Farmers have their own list:

1. "The septic tank is overflowing…." Not peculiar to farming but certainly a potential problem for those living away from mains sewerage. And it is not good man management to ask an employee to sort out unless he has caused it.

2. "The mart has called…." That nice heifer you sold at the spring sale has turned out to be in-calf and the buyer was not expecting or wanting to get two for the price of one.

3. "The grain merchant phoned…" And that 25 tonne lorry load of malting barley has been rejected because of high nitrogen, low nitrogen, screenings, not matching sample… or just sold too well.

4. "The potato merchant phoned…" And that consignment of Desiree seed potatoes you delivered into deepest Lincolnshire last week is showing signs of frost damage, latent tuber disease…or just sold too well.

5. "The Department – or The Scottish Government Rural Inspections and Directorate phoned…" To say that an official is coming to check the wages book. When you find it, make sure the hours worked tallies with the wages paid.

6. "An inspector is coming to do your annual audit for the Quality Assurance Scheme…." Cue abandoning everything else to ensure that spraying records, etc are up to date.

7. "The tractor with puncture…." After sending it and its driver to the furthest field from the steading via a busy main road, the driver phones to say there is a blow out and traffic is building up behind him.

The tractor with puncture

Slight problem

SCOTTISH-MADE TRACTORS

Although now sadly little but a memory, Scotland played its part in tractor production last century. Among the models to roll off production lines north of the Border were:

1. Rollo, Bonnybridge – the Rollo Croftmaster was first exhibited at the Highland Show in Edinburgh in 1955. While the main factory was at Bonnybridge, there were also branches at Easdale, Inverasdale, and in Wick. It was entered for the new implement award of the Highland Show in 1956 as the Rollo Croftmaster tractor fitted with new Rollo patented plough mounting linkage.

2. Massey Harris – started British production of its tractors at Manchester in 1948; one year later a new factory was opened at Kilmarnock to continue tractor production. About 50 tractors a week were being produced at this time. Phased out after links with Massey Ferguson in 1957.

3. Leyland and Nuffield, Bathgate – Nuffield Tractors had been started after World War II by Lord Nuffield, owner of Morris Motors Limited which had become part of BMC in 1951. Leyland tractors were created after the merger of the British Motor Corporation (BMC) with Leyland Motors to form British Leyland in 1968. In 1962 production of tractors began at Bathgate and continued until 1982. After selling to Nickerson, production moved to Gainsborough where Marshalls were made.

4. Reekie, Arbroath – built a cut-down Ferguson to fit between six-feet wide raspberry rows. Major engineering included cutting the half-shafts and front axles. When Harry Ferguson visited Arbroath he was less than happy with the Reekie badge above the Ferguson. The concept was later taken up by Ferguson and sold world-wide.

5. On-top Gillon – the tractor was based on a Bedford, the trailer was the back end of a Leyland Reiver, with a prop-shaft from tractor to trailer, so one had a driven axle on the tractor and two driven axles on the trailer; made at the company premises near Perth.

6. Glasgow, Cardonald – the Glasgow tractor was built by Wallace Farm Implements, Glasgow. It was a three-wheeler and was launched in 1919 but five years later ceased production when it lost out to the mass-produced Fordson.

7. Cuthbertson Water Buffalo – produced by James Cuthbertson of Biggar from about 1951 through to the 1960s. The tractor was an original design with the aim of working in very soft wet conditions and had a very low ground pressure.

8. Caterpillar, Uddingston – manufactured a range of heavy plant. Closed in 1987 having opened almost 30 years previously and employed 1,200 people, while hundreds more worked for other firms who depended on Caterpillar for work. At its peak it had employed 2,700 people.

A TOP TEN OF RSABI FUNDRAISING IN MODERN TIMES

There are a huge variety of fund raising efforts undertaken to raise funds for RSABI, from parties and balls to full-on adventure challenges. Here are a list of some of the most notable:

1. Walking the Southern Upland Way
Arthur Anderson, 1997

2. Overseas trekking
Peruvian Inca Trail 2004 and the Great Wall of China 2007

3. Driving a rough terrain vehicle around the UK coastline
Ian Henderson, August 2006

4. Ploughing at least 15 acres in every county
Plough Scotland, October 2008

5. Charity auction of semen and embryos, Texel Sheep Society
Lanark mart, August 2012

6. RSABI Great Glen Challenge 2012-2017
Annual multi-sport team challenge event for the agricultural industry

7. A fundraising gala lunch with BBC Countryfile's Adam Henson
With 175 VIP guests, October 2013

8. Vintage tractor restoration and raffle of a 1971 David Brown 780
Russell McNab and John McNae with Ayrshire Vintage Tractor and Machinery Club and Ayrshire RSABI voluntary committee, 2013/2014

9. The Royal Highlander horse-drawn stagecoach
Braemar to Aberdeen, Ewan MacInnes, August 2015

10. For the RSABI Help us help them Campaign 2016/17:
NC500 Solo Tractor Drive around the north coast of Scotland and Jack's Journey of British Auction Marts, John Meikle and Jack Walton, summer 2016

RSABI is grateful to all individuals, clubs and organisations who fundraise, sponsor and partner in support of such a worthy cause – alas far too many to mention everyone.

FARMING ON TELEVISION

For more than 40 years, *Landward* has been part of BBC Scotland's television schedules. Although now aimed at a general audience, for most of its life the programme was more sharply focussed on the social, economic, political and technical aspects of Scotland's farming industry.

In almost 1,000 programmes, it followed the changing seasons with reports from every corner of Scotland. Reflecting the ever-changing political and economic aspects of international farming and food production, *Landward* also reported from many countries with stories of relevance to Scotland. The programmes included:

1. Who'll be Here when the Trees Grow Tall – a film from the 1970s of the life of a Border hill farmer and his family in the Ettrick Valley where many farms were being taken over for forestry.

2. The Forsinard Experiment – on the Sutherland moors this film looked at the pioneering work of the Baird farming brothers who replaced native heather with grassland before drying the grass into pellets for livestock feed.

3. Fish Doctors to the World – in the 1980s this was the first film to look in depth at the work of the Institute of Aquaculture at Stirling University where scientists played a leading part in helping develop the Scottish fish farming industry.

4. Webster's Roup – from the 1990s this was the story of journalist Jack Webster at the roup at his late father's farm of Honeyneuk near Maud in Aberdeenshire; an emotional family history from the 1940s to the present day.

5. New Zealand – the first report from New Zealand where farm subsidies were withdrawn overnight, it looked at the challenge of farmers trying to develop new markets in the growing economies of the Pacific rim.

6. From Russia with Hope – as glasnost and perestroika took hold in the former Soviet Union in the mid 1980s, a group of young Russians came to Scotland to live on local farms in the hope that they would learn the art and practice of family farming and help break up the inefficient collective farms into economic units.

7. Taim Bilong Hangri – the title is pidgin English for 'famine' and this film in 1990 followed two young people from Scotland who tried to create more sustainable food production in Papua New Guinea – one with sheep production in the Central Highlands and the other with improving fish stocks on the Sepik River in the north of the country. This film went on to win the One World Broadcasting Trust's top award for UK documentaries.

8. China and Vietnam – two films in successive years with Aberdeen-based Professor Bob Orskov underlining the importance of self-help in rural communities.

TOP FARMING POP SONGS

Farming appears to have featured in the pop charts, but beware as some of the titles are misleading and the lyrics give the game away…

1. 'I've Got a Brand New Combine Harvester' The Wurzels
A lyric involving bribery – "I've got a brand new combine harvester and I'll give you the key" and animal cruelty – "I threw me pitchfork at your dog." All being driven by a desire to increase the size of a farm.

2. 'Fields of Gold' Sting
A love story set in a field of barley just before combining. It omits any advice on important issues such as checking moisture levels in the grain.

3. 'Me and The Farmer' The Housemartins
This is not for farmers who are accused of, among other things, being crooks and "chopping down sheep and ripping up fields".

4. 'Country Trash' Johnny Cash
A song of comparative success at farming – "I got about a dollar stacked away" by the man in black.

5. 'Size of a Cow' The Wonderstuff
This is not based on the remarks of a livestock judge at a show. It is based on lots of regrets which are "the size of a cow".

6. 'Fields of Fire' Big Country
It may seem to hark back to the days when fields of straw were burnt, but this anthem is more an evocation of World War I.

7. 'Harvest for the World' The Isley Bros
Not a call for more grain to be grown around the globe but a plea for more even distribution of wealth.

8. 'Three Little Pigs' Green Jelly
Nothing to do with pig production. This is more an updated version of the children's nursery rhyme.

9. 'Dust Bowl Blues' Woody Guthrie
With Scottish weather, it is most unlikely this would happen in this country.

10. 'No Milk Today' Herman's Hermits
Not so much a reaction to poor milk prices or an instruction on the shopping list, more a lament for a lost love.

CELEBRITY CHEFS OF THEIR DAY

Life in the kitchen in the 1920s was much more basic and economical than nowadays where top chefs are awarded celebrity status and their own tv programmes. A Scottish Women's Rural Institutes cookery handbook from that era which sold tens of thousands of copies, lists hundreds of recipes with nary a mention of a drizzle of this or a soupcon of that. Among the hundreds of recipes of those more frugal days were:

1. Cabbage soup where the main ingredients are, unsurprisingly, cabbages and water, with the former being boiled up in the latter with only a sprinkling of salt to be added to the resulting soup.

2. Poor man's goose – a mixture of suet, onions, sage and salt along with some fatty bacon. When mixed and rolled up together in a floured pudding cloth, it was then boiled for up to two hours. Note no sign of a goose being involved.

3. Sago soup – bad news for those who thought sago only appeared as pudding. An elementary mixing up of fine sago and egg yolk in a good stock took it almost to completion. Cream was added before serving, the recipe comments.

4. Sheep's head broth "Clean the head thoroughly, remove the brains and put head on fire in pan of cold water. When approaching boiling, add vegetables. Cook thoroughly then lift out head and cut meat into small pieces. Take out tongue and thicken soup with flour." So far this has not been demonstrated on tv.

5. Brain cakes – the brains were not wasted as a later recipe recommends blanching them and then boiling until tender in milk. After chopping them up, add bread crumbs, pepper, parsley and salt and then, with beaten egg to moisten them flatten out into cakes. A covering of bread crumbs and then the cakes went into the fat fryer until they were a crisp brown. Scrumptious.

6. Crappit heid "Take four large cod heads and boil until all the fish leaves the bones. Remove the bones and stew the fish until brown. Season with pepper and serve on toast or oatcakes."

7. Dinner for five for three days from a sheep's pluck
Mrs Beeton's Cookery book observed, "First catch your hare", but here it is "procure a nice sheep's pluck thoroughly cleaned;" a pluck being the heart, lungs, lights and liver.
     Day one instructions – slice liver and fry with onions. After covering the liver with flour, serve with boiled potatoes. Meanwhile the remainder of the pluck is boiled for three and a half hours to obtain a fine stock.
     Day two – make haggis with remainder of liver and the lights. Serve with mashed potatoes.
     Day three – use stock to make lentil soup and use suet for dumplings.

BLACKFACE SHEEP

The Blackface is the most numerous pure breed in Britain, with most found in Scotland. It is one of the hardiest breeds, and the backbone of the Scottish sheep industry. All Blackfaces are horned, with black or black and white face and legs. As a maternal hill breed, females have a strong mothering ability to rear lambs in extreme terrain. The breed is easily hefted, making it ideal for large areas of hill country and able to produce sheep for every climatic condition, thanks to the different distinct types within the breed, which have evolved over the years influenced by climate, environment and grazing quality.

The North (Perth) type is found mainly in Northeast Scotland, Southwest England and Northern Ireland. The South type, which is an integration of Lanark and Newton Stewart bloodlines, is dominant in much of Scotland and areas of Ireland, and is the mother of the ever-popular Scotch Mule. In the North of England the Northumberland Blackface is popular and influential in breeding the North of England Mule.

Top priced rams (up to December 2016)

1. £160,000 Dalmally, 2015 from I. Hunter, Dalchirla to Elmscleugh, Auldhouseburn and Crossflatt.

2. £100,000 Lanark, 2014 from A. MacArthur & Sons, Nunnerie to Elmscleugh.

3. £90,000 Lanark, 2014 from T. Renwick & Sons, Blackhouse to Nunnerie, Crossflatt and Auldhouseburn.

4. £90,000 Dalmally, 2012 from I. Hunter, Dalchirla to Elmscleugh, Glenrath and Auldhouseburn.

5. £90,000 Dalmally, 2010 from I. Hunter, Dalchirla to Nunnerie, Midlock and Connachan.

6. £85,000 Lanark, 1997 from Neil McCall Smith, Connachan to Dalchirla.

7. £85,000 Lanark, 2016 from W. Dunlop, Elmscleugh to Auldhouseburn and Glenrath.

8. £68,000 Lanark, 2013 from W. Dunlop, Elmscleugh to Nunnerie, Loughash, Gass, Dalchirla, Midlock and Blackcraig.

9. £68,000 Dalmally, 2015 from I. Hunter, Dalchirla to Harestone, Troloss and Whelphill.

CHAPTER TWELVE

SCOTTISH SPORTSMEN/WOMEN
WITH A RURAL CONNECTION

1. Jim Clark MBE
Formula One Champion in 1963 and 1965. He had 72 Grand prix starts and 25 wins. Jim also won the Indianapolis 500 in 1965. He is widely regarded as one of the most gifted motor racing drivers of all time. His home was the family farm of Edington Mains, Chirnside, Berwickshire.

2. Ian Stirling
Played for Arbroath Football Club and was captain before eventually becoming chairman. He made 371 first team appearances, scoring 41 goals mostly as inside forward; he latterly played at centre half. Ian has headed the farm business at Dickmontlaw just outside Arbroath; his business interests also included a joinery and milk bar.

3. David Sinclair CBE
Farmed an arable stock enterprise at Abernyte on the northern slopes of the Carse of Gowrie. He was a notable cattle expert and showman, winning the Supreme Championship at Smithfield in 1963, 1968 and 1971. His other interest was in potatoes where he claimed there was only one thing better than one potato on his plate, and that was two potatoes. He was chairman of the Potato Marketing Board. David was a lifelong supporter of Dundee United who he played for in his youth.

4. Richard Swan
Captained Scotland at cricket from 1982 until 1992, gaining 90 caps. He was a right-hand batsman and right arm medium pace bowler. Richard farms at Blackhouse Farm, Eyemouth with his wife Jeanna, Lord Lieutenant of Berwickshire.

5. Laura Muir
A student of veterinary medicine at the University of Glasgow. She is a middle-distance runner who won gold medals in 2017 in the 1,500m and 3,000m at the European Indoor Championships.

6. Samantha (Sammi) Kinghorn
Paralysed from the waist down by a roof-fall of snow on the family farm at Middlethird, Gordon, Berwickshire, when helping her father clear paths, in December 2010 when 14. She has fought back to become a top wheelchair athlete and, at 21, won golds in the 100

and 200 metre sprints at the World Para Athletics in London in summer 2017, plus a bronze in another sprint. She is now training to take part in a wheelchair marathon.

7. Edith Barnes

Gardener at Drummond Castle and the daughter of a retired gamekeeper. She has won a string of British, European and World championships in clay pigeon shooting. In 1992, Beretta named her shooter of the year, the first woman to be given that award.

8. Jim McAlister

Brought up on his parents' farm on the Isle of Bute where his first job was delivering milk from his father's dairy. He is a professional footballer playing in the midfield, and has been with several Scottish clubs before moving to Blackpool in 2015.

9. Louise Aitken-Walker MBE

A Borders farmer's daughter, she learned to drive on the farm at an early age, and was entered in a 'find a lady driver' competition by her brothers which proved to be the start of a very successful career. She starred in both rallying and saloon car racing; the pinnacle of her career saw her become Ladies World Rally Champion in 1990.

ROSTRUM RHETORIC

One of the features of the auction selling system is the chat between the auctioneer and the seller as, between them, they try to raise enthusiasm for the animal about to be sold. Listed below are a few well-known phrases designed to get buyers into a bidding frenzy:

1. "The first one's always the cheapest" A plea to get the show underway at a reasonable level as every potential bidder hangs back to see what the trade is going to do.

2. "These tups have never seen a cabbage" Popular comment with one breed that is reputed to be able to munch its way through mountains of cabbages.

3. "The best I have ever bred" Often stated as if it were true.

4. "These beasts will shift like snow off a dyke" Reserved for when a particularly scrawny group come into the ring.

5. "Real active tup will go the top of any hill" As the beast throws itself at the barriers, "You will never catch it," is not mentioned.

6. "This bull has been to the party and knows how to dance" A euphemism for experience.

7. "This bull can serve nervous heifers on black ice" This sales pitch actually caught the imagination and helped sell the bull.

8. "It's no enough" Universal complaint by sellers who have dreamt their livestock are much better than they are in reality.

9. "Just off the heather" Again a favourite saying when a pen of 'leaner' stock come into the ring.

10. "Out of the best ewe on the place" Almost entirely fictional comment.

11. "They are fed on neeps and straw" Everyone can see they are typical examples of the "plainer types were more difficult to cash" auction report comment.

12. "You'll never see fitter cattle, they've been running with the stags on Jura" An opening pitch heard at the Oban Highland cattle sales.

13. "He is on his honeymoon and he'll not be caring what they make" Again from the Oban sales, but this time from a stockman trusted with the job of getting a good price for his boss's cattle.

TOP TEN CLYDESDALE STALLIONS

Right up to the 1950s, the Clydesdale horse provided the horsepower on farms. The breed relied on top stallions to supply strong working horses and ten of the best were:

1. Barons Pride (foaled 1890) From the Darnley line and did more to improve the wearing qualities of feet and legs than any other sire. Baron of Buchlyvie, Everlasting and Revelanta were his best sons, he also sired lots of good mares; many of them were in the Harviestoun stud.

2. Hiawatha (1892) From the Prince of Wales line, he was a slow developer but matured into the best show horse of its time. Owing to different rules at that time, Hiawatha won the Cawdor cup four times. Apukwa Marcellus and Hiawatha Again were great breeding sons. Boquhan Lady Peggy was an outstanding daughter.

3. Baron of Buchlyvie (1900) A horse of great style and quality. Sold for the record price of £9,500 at 11 years old, he died prematurely as the result of his fore leg being broken by a kick from a mare. His skeleton is preserved in the Kelvingrove art gallery and museum.

4. Dunure Footprint (1908) Recognised as the most prolific and best breeding stallion in Clydesdale history. Popular present day sires directly descended from Dunure Footprint sons include Dillers Top Gun from Kismet and Arradoul Balvenie from Dunraven.

5. Benefactor (1922) A grandson of Hiawatha Again and the leading sire immediately after Dunure Footprint (the sire of his dam). Benefactor was the perfect combination of style, quality, weight and substance.

6. Craigie Beau Ideal (1929) A grandson of Bonnie Buchlyvie, he is the most successful show horse listed here, winning championships at the Highland and Royal shows as well as four supreme championships at the national stallion show.

7. Muirton Sensation (1950) Descended from Hiawatha Again on the male line, he is regarded by the older generation of Clydesdale breeders as the best and most true-to-type Clydesdale stallion to date.

8. Doura Excelsior (1964) Descended from Dunure Footprints' son Kismet, he was the most popular and best breeding sire from the late 1960s to the late 1970s. His progeny were characterised by great weight and substance. Many of his best sons and daughters were exported to North America.

9. Doura Masterstroke (1974) Descended on the main line from Muirton Monarch, his dam being by Doura Excelsior. He was a true breeder's horse, with perfectly flat bone and tremendous hind action. Although he left some excellent males, he probably left the most regular bunch of females by any sire.

10. Collessie Cut Above (1992) Descended from the Dunure Footprint son, Dunraven. His dam was from probably the most successful line of mares in the breed. Cut Above has been the leading Clydesdale sire since the late 1990s; his sons and daughter have been widely exported and Cut Above is a major influence on the breed world-wide. Collessie Whinhill President and Highfield Collessie are among his best-known sons.

MODERN LANGUAGE

10 modern words that a farmer over 60 may need clarity on:

1. iPad – not an optical bandage. iPad is a line of tablet computers designed, developed and marketed by Apple Inc. The first iPad was released in 2010.

2. Online – not for hanging recently washed clothes on. Online was originally a magazine for information systems first published in 1977, now shorthand for information on the internet.

3. Apple Mac – not a mid-morning healthy snack. The Mackintosh branded Mac was introduced in 1998 and is a series of personal computers designed, developed and marketed by Apple Inc.

4. Blackberry – not for making jam. BlackBerry is a Canadian-based multinational company focussed on wireless telecommunication now specialising in Enterprise software.

5. Tablets – not what the doctor ordered. A tablet is a mobile computer with a touchscreen display in a single flat package.

6. Android – not found on Dr Who. Android is a mobile operating system developed by Google and designed primarily for touchscreen mobile devices.

7. Cookie – not a mid-afternoon snack. An HTTP cookie is a small piece of data sent from a website and stored on the user's computer by the user's web browser while the user is browsing.

8. Java – not a cup of coffee. Java is a general purpose computer programming language that is specifically designed to have as few implementation dependencies as possible.

9. Twitter – not something birds do. It is a hugely popular social media site where people communicate in 140 characters or less, with Donald Trump a keen user.

10. Spam – not for eating between two slices of bread. Spam is an unsolicited or undesired electronic message, despite the fact the sender may be generously offering to put millions of pounds into your bank account.

FARMING CHILDREN'S STORIES

Right from the cradle, there is no escape from farming-linked stories. Some children inspired by Richard Adam's *Watership Down* go on to become conservationists, or at the very least want to buy a bunny of their own. Others, after reading this classic, will only want to see a rabbit in a pie.

This list is purely subjective. Everyone has their personal favourites and their children and grandchildren are likely to have entirely different ones.

1. *The Tale of Peter Rabbit* by Beatrix Potter
Disobedient rabbit incurs the wrath of keen gardener Mr McGregor – and who could blame him.

2. *The Very Hungry Caterpillar* by Eric Carle
Many legged beastie munches his way through this pesticide/insecticide free book.

3. *The Enormous Turnip*, a traditional folk tale
A knowledgeable countryman (or woman) plants a turnip seed and requires the co-operative effort of half the countryside to get the fully-grown turnip uprooted.

4. *The Tale of Jemima Puddle-Duck* by Beatrix Potter
Perhaps she's not the most astute of ducks, but in her quest to look after her own clutch of eggs Jemima engages the services of a helpful fox.

5. *The Apple Tree Farm* books by Heather Amery
The adventures of Mrs Boot the farmer, her children Poppy and Sam, Rusty the dog and Woolly the sheep. And of course, looking for the small duck on every page helps too.

6. *Charlotte's Web* by E.B. White
Describes the relationship between Charlotte the helpful and kind spider and Wilbur the pig who is somewhat reluctant to end up on the dinner plate.

7. *Fantastic Mr Fox* by Roald Dahl
Wily fox pits his wits against farmers Boggis, Bunce and Bean.

8. *Floss* by Kim Lewis
Town dog becomes sheepdog.

9. *The True Story of the Three Little Pigs* by Jon Scieszka
The much-maligned wolf of the original tale puts the story right.

10. *Farmer Boy* by Laura Ingalls Wilder
19th century New York State but the changing seasons, endless chores and pure hard work still strikes a chord.

11. *Old Farm – New Farm*
A morality tale, lovingly illustrated, about a young farmer taking over a neglected farm with the full co-operation of the neglected animals.

12. *Little Red Hen*
A multi-tasking hen who grew her own crop of wheat to make bread, a lesson in self-sufficiency.

Farming children's stories

SCOTTISH AGRICULTURAL INSTITUTIONS OF THE PAST

There are a whole lot of organisations and institutions which played an important role in Scottish agriculture – and often globally – which no longer exist in their original form:

1. The Macaulay Institute for Soil Research – founded in 1930 and based at Craigiebuckler, Aberdeen, its aim was to improve the productivity of Scottish agriculture. It was established with a gift of £10,000 from Thomas Bassett Macaulay, a Scot living in Canada who was part of the Sun Life Assurance Company. It merged with the Hill Farm Research Organisation in 1987, relocating to a new site at Bucksburn, Aberdeen. In April 2011, it merged with the Scottish Crop Research Institute to become the James Hutton Institute.

2. The Scottish Crop Research Institute – now part of the James Hutton Institute, it was based on 172ha at Invergowrie near Dundee. The site opened in 1951 as the Scottish Horticultural Research Institute, merging with the Scottish Plant Breeding Station in 1981 to become SCRI, and in 1987, it also took on the Scottish Agricultural Statistics Service.

3. North of Scotland College of Agriculture, East of Scotland College of Agriculture and West of Scotland College of Agriculture – all three had very separate identities, and graduates of each of them certainly believed that 'theirs' was the best. All three are now part of SRUC, which also now includes Barony, Oatridge and Elmwood colleges. Besides straight agriculture, students can now study any one of 117 courses on subjects as diverse as sport and tourism and at all levels.

4. The Rowett Research Institute – while the Rowett still exists, it now focusses on the relationship between food, diet and human health, and is much less involved in animal nutrition, which was one of its key aims when it was set up in 1913 by Dr John Boyd Orr, its founding director. Previously based at Bucksburn on the outskirts of Aberdeen, it is now part of Aberdeen University and relocated to a new building at the medical school in 2016.

5. The Hannah Research Institute – set up in 1928 as a dairy research institute, the Hannah became a world-renowned centre for research into animal physiology and dairy science. However, amid wrangling about management and a review of research in Scotland, its government funding was withdrawn, and it closed in 2006.

MUSICAL FARMERS

1. Ian Powrie (1923-2011) – born at Whitehouse Farm, Strathardle. When his band turned professional in 1960, it became one of the mainstays on BBC Television's iconic White Heather Club, appearing on 86 of its 100-show run. Ian also became musical director for entertainer Andy Stewart.

2. Bill Black (1935-2016) – born on a farm at Muthill, near Crieff, Bill's was one of the busiest bands on the scene for many years, travelling the length and breadth of the country. Noted as a 'workaholic' Bill owned an animal health business with branches in Aberfeldy, Oban and Inverness.

3. Gordon Pattullo – from Tullybaccart near Coupar Angus, he was at one time Andy Stewart's accordionist and then his musical director. For ten years Gordon was involved in theatre shows almost every week. He also has many fine compositions to his credit.

4. Jimmy Lindsay – farming at Amulree, Dunkeld, Jimmy is a past winner of the coveted 'All Scotland Accordion Championship' at Perth in 1959.

5. Willie Simpson – a farmer from Glenalmond, he has played the fiddle and led a band for a lifetime. Most readers in East Central Scotland will have danced to Willie and his band at YFC dances, weddings and parties.

6. Paul Anderson – fiddler and former dairy farmer from Tarland. An afficionado on all music and culture of the North East. He is a respected tutor and composer, having composed music for many TV shows.

7. Jimmy Burgess – a dairy farmer and has played in bands in Shetland for more than 50 years. He famously stood up to the mighty Tesco and refused to supply it with milk one winter when ferries were irregular, until he was sure his own customers were fully supplied.

8. Colin Campbell – farmer, entertainer, accordionist and mimic from Fochabers. 'Colin Campbell's Local Radio' are best-selling videos and DVDs of his humour, music and social comment.

9. Fergus Wood – a sheep farmer, tourist operator and local councillor. He plays accordion and is the founder, manager and player in the Kinlochard ceilidh band.

10. Peter Kerr – the prolific author of the Mallorcan Oranges books, and led the Clyde Valley Stompers in his youth. He and his family farmed in East Lothian.

11. Simon Howie – built a meat processing factory on his Findony farm which, together with the retail side, is now a massive business. He plays accordion in his Scottish dance band.

12. Bruce MacGregor – leader of 'Blazing Fiddles', Bruce set up a music archive and music venue at his Bogbain Farm at Inverness. Presents "Travelling Folk" on BBC Radio Scotland.

13. Freeland Barbour – from Bonskeid and Mains of Fincastle at Pitlochry, he is leader of 'The Occasionals' and the Wallochmor ceilidh band. Former producer of "Take the Floor".

14. Tony Reid (1926-2015) – a farmer, accordionist and leader of the original 'Glendaruel Band', from Balnakilly at Strathardle.

15. Nicol McLaren – from Blairgowrie, he is leader of the Glencraig Scottish dance band, and is well known as an agricultural rep, as is Gordon Howe who plays in his band.

16. Neil Caul – an accordionist and noted judge of cattle.

17. Hamish Polson – plays in the Strathpeffer Scottish dance band and is a noted Aberdeen Angus breeder.

DISCUSSIONS WITH THE BANK MANAGER

For those farming with borrowings – about two thirds of farmers – the visit to the bank to explain differences between the well-crafted forward cash flow and the reality brings a frisson of challenge to even the most imaginative customer. Below are some of the reasons why the cash flow predictions have not turned into fact, looking instead as a piece of optimistic fantasy:

1. "Bulls did not make as much as I thought they would"
Despite breeders' best efforts employing stockmanship and science, all bulls do not turn out to be world beaters.

2. "Store lambs were very cheap, so bought some more instead of selling what I had"
This sort of excuse could easily elicit the bank manager's response, "Let's go back to the former arrangement where you bank with us".

3. "I couldn't resist buying store cattle at that price"
There is strange fever which affects some farmers in the spring when the grass begins to grow. All carefully constructed budgets go out of their heads when faced with a ring full of growthy stirks at what looks like a bargain price.

4. "The supermarket buyer has just told me that they are extending their payment terms"
Despite the fact that most farm produce is only on the shelves for a few days, supermarkets seem to need an increasing number of weeks before returning the grower his or her share.

5. "EU payment didn't arrive when it was promised"
Scottish Government has had its problems with the computer responsible for making payments on time and has offered interest-free loans, so this excuse could easily have the bank manager saying, "I don't believe the figures, but I admire your ingenuity".

6. "The potato market collapsed"
The thousand tonnes of baking quality ware potatoes which you were holding in cold store hoping that the price would hit the forecast £300 per tonne were now worth a fraction of that as stockfeed.

7. "Malting barley rejected"
The 20 hectare field of malting barley which you contracted at a price leaving a reasonable margin has been harvested and sampled but the nitrogen is too high or too many splits or too high screenings; it is now only feeding quality at two thirds of the price.

8. "The sun didn't shine"
You budgeted for 30 weeks occupancy for holiday cottages and even in the south of England figures are in the low twenties.

9. "Weather was too good"
You have a contracting business with a full range of harvesting machinery but the summer and early autumn were so good that farmers were able to get by without your assistance.

10. "Kept grain until May as I get £10/t more"
Quite a frequent occurrence, apparently, but the farmer never thinks about his HP that is due the preceding November.

'Store lambs very cheap so bought some more instead of selling what I had.'

FARMING PAPERS WHICH ARE NO MORE

Despite the fact most kitchen tables in farmhouses are groaning under the weight of farming papers, there are some which have gone to the great recycling bin in the sky, but which are missed by their loyal readers who still talk about them now.

1. *Farming News* – a tabloid in size and attitude. It gave a pithy round-up of the week's news, and was guaranteed to shake things up when it took on an issue. Launched in the 1980s, it closed in August 2001, hard hit by the downturn in farming and the foot and mouth crisis.

2. *North British Agriculturist* – established in the 1860s and became the *Farming News* in 1931. It was formerly owned by the Anderson family and in the 1960s a gentleman of the old school called Brewis Anderson still wrote for it. Noted contributors included John R. Allan, (Charlie Allan's dad) author of Farmer's Boy and Fordyce Maxwell, who started his career there, while both Ronnie Fraser and Ian Morrison were editors. It closed in 1970.

3. *Power Farming* – loved by any farmer with an interest in horsepower not of the four-legged type. Focussed on tests and new machinery, it was incorporated into *Farmers Weekly* in the 1990s as a monthly feature, and then superceded by an online subscription service which ran for a short time. Back issues still do a good trade on EBay.

4. *Agribusiness Scotland* – started by Eddie Gillanders, who subsequently set up *Farm North East*, this popular magazine was sold to a Glasgow-based publishing house and edited by now-NFUS communications director Bob Carruth.

5. *Big Farm Weekly* – launched on the market in 1976, this weekly tabloid provided hard-hitting news. It was bought by Farmers Weekly's publishers and subsequently closed in 1992.

6. *Farmer and Stockbreeder* – a weekly publication which launched in 1889, it merged with the NFU's British Farmer magazine in 1971, becoming the British Farmer and Stockbreeder. It closed in 1984 due to loss of advertising revenue.

7. *Crops* and its sister title, *Stock* – these fortnightly magazines, launched in the late 1980s, were ground-breaking tabloids at the time with their use of colour. *Stock* ceased publishing in the early 1990s, with *Crops* disappearing only last year.

8. *Pig Farming* – like the wood stain, it did what it said on the tin. Launched in 1953 and published out of Ipswich, it was a technical magazine and also featured some well-thought of columnists. It closed in the 1990s.

9 Farmgate.com and Globalfarmers.com – two websites launched in the dotcom boom which burned through vast sums of cash in their quest to revolutionise farming and how farmers did business. UBM, owner of Farmgate, closed it in 2001, while Globalfarmers went into receivership in the same year.

RSABI HELP LIST

1. Financial help – RSABI assists those in need by issuing food vouchers, organising essential household items, training, essential travel costs, disability aids and helps with the applications and costs of necessary business reviews, among others. It also helps by maximising income through benefits, referring to other appropriate charities and looking at fuel initiatives to save costs.

2. Emotional support – RSABI is here when the normal pressures of life get too much. Whether family, money health or business issues, it is a non-judgemental listening ear. RSABI can find services available locally to help and support with the cost, if appropriate.

3. Business difficulties – support for working farmers when they need it. Signposting to relevant support, getting an appropriate volunteer to help or using its network of partners to give callers some options and solutions. It can also help fund a business review if required.

4. Health issues – this can be physical as well as mental wellbeing. It can help look at how changes in health can be managed and whether there are benefits or agencies that may support the caller's changed situation. Referral to appropriate partners to ensure that there is support in place and supporting families of those with health issues to be able to visit their loved ones are other essential forms of help.

5. Family/personal issues – helping people look at succession planning and giving pointers on the steps to consider. It is a confidential listening service that can help find local resources to assist the situation, such as mediation services.

6. State benefit enquiries – life changes that impact health or wealth such as change of job, reduced hours, unemployment, redundancy, retirement, illness and having a baby are some of the stages in life that may impact income. It can point people in the right direction to ensure that they get their full entitlement.

7. Debt problems – debt can affect mood and relationships. RSABI can help by supporting people to access local agencies to deal with the situation. It can provide assistance by ensuring essential household needs are met, allowing the time to get a solution in place, and reducing pressure on the family. It has volunteers who can support clients by attending appointments.

8. Employment issues – RSABI can give support on redundancy, sickness benefits and other work issues.

9. Housing issues – RSABI gives direction on where to get help with housing issues, whether people are being forced to move or looking to relocate. It can give local information to support those with housing problems, including energy saving initiatives.

10. Help with paperwork – it has a team of case officers and volunteers which can be used to help read, explain or complete paperwork.

THE DOZEN MOST INFLUENTIAL
PEOPLE IN SCOTTISH AGRICULTURE

This is possibly the most contentious list as many people may want to see their names appear on it or even expect to see themselves mentioned. The criteria for inclusion included being alive and active. Politicians were not considered. Neither were a slew of successful business people who are mentioned in another list.

With these provisos, the deciding panel, who wished anonymity, came up with the following names. They are not in any order as that might lead to further dispute.

1. John Cameron has been at the top of agricultural politics for more than four decades, during which time he has embraced politicians of the main four parties in Scotland. He made his name initially as NFUS president in fighting the French ban on sheep imports. At one time, he was reputed to be the biggest sheep farmer in Europe with more than 10,000 ewes on his hill units and his base in Fife. Train driver in his spare time.

2. Professor Julie Fitzpatrick skilfully heads up the world famous Moredun Institute, keeping its independence and reputation for the highest levels of research in animal health and welfare. She also holds among a host of other appointments and honours, the chair in Food Security in the College of Medical, Veterinary and Life Sciences at the University of Glasgow. Professor Fitzpatrick's research interests focus on livestock health and disease in the UK and in developing countries.

3. James Graham has been chief executive of SAOS since 1998. SAOS is the membership body of 65 agricultural co-operatives trading in Scotland, whose collective throughput in 2016 exceeded £2.2 billion. James has held positions as company secretary, advisor, consultant, chief executive and non-executive director in the co-op agri-food sector for 33 years. He is an acknowledged specialist in agricultural co-operatives and supply chain collaboration in the food and drink industry.

4. Jonnie Hall, NFU Scotland's director of policy, has been involved with agricultural and rural policy for more than 30 years. A proud Geordie, he is a graduate of the University of Newcastle and Oxford University. Following an academic and consultancy career, Jonnie joined what was the Scottish Landowners' Federation in January 1998, leading their policy work on agriculture and land use issues. He then joined NFU Scotland in May 2007, and has overall responsibility for the policy work of the Union.

5. Eddie Gillanders has served the agricultural industry for more than 50 years as one of the top reporters. Despite being past his three score years and ten, his output, energy and enthusiasm is unequalled in the press ranks. His own magazine, Farm North East, which is virtually all his and his wife, Marion's own efforts is highly regarded. In addition, he undertakes press relation jobs with farm organisations, as well as being behind trips abroad for some of his readership. His has received a bag full of awards and honours from both his fellow journalists and the agricultural community. He does have a particular soft spot for the Aberdeen Angus breed.

6. Jim McLaren, the fast-talking and even faster walking chairman of Quality Meat Scotland has been influential in guiding the livestock sector through changes in support policies while simultaneously beating the drum for Scotch Beef and Lamb and Specially Selected Pork. This follows a stint as NFU Scotland president where he was instrumental in raising the profile of this organisation.

7. James Withers is a young man on a mission. As head of Scotland Food and Drink, he is at the sharp end of ensuring ambitious output figures are achieved. The latest target is £30 billion of food and drink by the year 2030. For comparison, the output was £10 billion a decade ago. Previously he was chief executive of NFU Scotland.

8. Nigel Millar, one of the best brains of this generation, did a stint as president of NFU Scotland, where, as befitted a qualified vet and practising farmer, he took a pro-active role in dealing with animal diseases as well as dealing with the introduction of the most complex iterations of the Common Agricultural Policy. One former president said Millar had 'lifted the bar in respect of disease awareness and control'. He now chairs a Scottish Government committee on animal health.

9. Graham Bruce is the peppery driving force behind Ringlink, the leading labour and machinery co-operative in Scotland. Since its inception, in 1988, Bruce has been at its helm. He has seen its membership rise to more than 2,000 and has innovatively expanded its range of services. Of special mention has to be his encouragement for a new generation of youngsters to come and work in the farming industry.

10. Jim Walker rose to prominence leading a farmers' protest at Stranraer, but is most remembered as the leader of the NFUS during the 2001 foot and mouth outbreak, where he made often controversial but ultimately successful policies that curbed and conquered the disease in Scotland while it still continued in England. Universally known as Walker the Talker on account of his skill as an orator, he continues to express strident views on today's agricultural policies and those who make them.

11. Professor Jim Hunter has raised the profile of Scotland's crofting community. He is the author of the seminal work, *The Making of the Crofting Community*, which has been followed by a number of other distinguished books on aspects of crofting history. In the 1980s, he was the first director of the Scottish Crofting Federation but is now Professor of History at the University of the Highlands and Islands. Sandwiched between these posts, Hunter was chairman of the Highlands and Islands Enterprise Board, charged with responsibility for the area's economic regeneration.

12. You – for all those who thought they should be on this list, please insert your name now along with a short list of your multiple achievements.

ALSO BY ANDREW ARBUCKLE

Footsteps in the Furrow
We Waved to the Baker
Sparks from the Smiddy
Local Hero – Dave Rollo

AND BY JOHN AND ANDREW ARBUCKLE

The First One Hundred years – the story of NFU Scotland
Farming is a Funny Business – compilation of 300 stories

Kerry knows her donation makes a big difference to someone struggling to cope.

RSABI
Supporting People in Scottish Agriculture

RSABI
Supporting People in Scottish Agriculture
INDIVIDUAL SUPPORTER

Join our supporter scheme for as little as £25/year. Call 0300 111 4166.

Email: rsabi@rsabi.org.uk

www.rsabi.org.uk

Scottish Charity No. SC009828

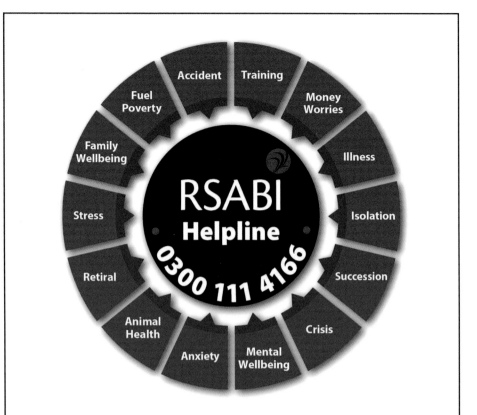

RSABI provides practical support and financial assistance to individuals and their families across the agricultural sector including farming, crofting, and growing.

Established in 1897 under Royal patronage, RSABI has supported generations of people in agriculture. The charity has evolved over time in order to remain relevant and fit for purpose for the challenges people in the industry face today.

Contact our helpline on 0300 111 4166
7am – 11pm every day of the year

Help us help them – RSABI relies on donations from generous individuals, businesses, organisations and trusts. This support is vital and enables us to continue our valuable work supporting people in Scottish agriculture.

RSABI The Rural Centre West Mains of Ingliston Newbridge EH28 8LT
rsabi@rsabi.org.uk   0300 111 4166   www.rsabi.org.uk

Scottish Charity No.SC009828

RSABI
Supporting People
in Scottish Agriculture

www.rsabi.org.uk

Scottish Charity No. SC009828